LET ME COUNT

HUMAN HORIZONS SERIES

LET ME COUNT

Dorothy M. Jeffree

A CONDOR BOOK
SOUVENIR PRESS (E & A LTD)

Copyright © 1989 by Dorothy M. Jeffree

First published 1989 by Souvenir Press
(Educational & Academic) Ltd,
43 Great Russell Street, London WC1B 3PA
and simultaneously in Canada

ISBN 0 285 65080 7 hardback
ISBN 0 285 65081 5 paperback

Photoset, printed and bound in Great Britain by
WBC Bristol and Maesteg

ACKNOWLEDGEMENTS

I would like to thank Sue Fagg and her staff at Piper Hill
School for their help and co-operation in trying out the ideas
in this book, and also Pam Maddock and the staff of Wargrave
House School, Newton-le-Willows. I would also like to thank
Jennifer Warner for her helpful comments and support in the
writing of this book.

I am grateful to Octopus Books for permission to quote the
passage on p. 148 from *A Parent's Guide to Your Child's Maths*
by Ruth Merrtens, published by The Parent and Child
Programme, 1988.

CONTENTS

INTRODUCTION

You don't count!

This is a very hurtful remark which we would not wish to be directed at any of our children.

This book is intended for all parents and teachers who would like to help their children 'count for something' in life, and to help them cope with the numerical relationships between the things around them. I have used the title 'teacher' throughout, not just in the professional sense of 'schoolteacher', but to denote anyone, be it parents, grandparents, siblings, neighbours or friends, who helps a child to learn.

The book is aimed at the parents and teachers of *any* young child up to primary school age. In addition, I have had in mind those children (who may be older) who have special needs and are experiencing difficulties in learning for whatever reason. These difficulties may be severe and include other areas of learning as well as number, or they may be moderate or even shortlived and mainly concerning numeracy.

Do not be put off reading this book because you are 'no good at maths'. You are almost certainly better at it than you think if you can follow a game of tennis, a recipe or a knitting pattern, know how many days there are till Christmas, find your favourite programme in the *Radio Times*, play cards or go shopping.

UNDERSTANDING

Today's emphasis in the teaching of mathematics is on promoting understanding and the ability to solve practical problems, rather than in copying one particular way of doing a sum. Even in this age of computers and calculators, understanding is as important as ever. Remember, there are no short cuts to understanding: it dawns gradually, through experience.

Pamela Liebeck (1984) reminded us of the developmental stages of early childhood.

At first a baby learns through the *active* exploration of the world of sound, touch, sight, smell and taste. He explores whatever comes into his ken by mouthing, scratching, dropping, pushing or shaking. At the same time he will be hearing simple *language* centred around the activity of the moment. He will gradually form links between whatever he is investigating and its name, for example, the word 'rattle'.

At the next stage he will begin to form mental *pictures* of his previous activities and also to recognise external *pictures* of objects (for example, a picture of a rattle). Not until much later will he be able to recognise abstract *symbols* like the letters R/A/T/T/L/E as standing for the real object.

A child must go through the same sequence of stages every time in order to arrive at a real *understanding* of numerical concepts.

It is rather like climbing a mountain: in order to reach the summit you must always start at the bottom.

That is why I have chosen the initials which spell out a mountain range—ALPS—to denote the sequence of stages in learning to understand.

A ACTIVE involvement
L LANGUAGE of the activity
P PICTURING the activity
S SYMBOLS of the activity

As in mountain climbing, this learning must be a corporate venture. Sometimes the adult follows the child's lead and sometimes it is the other way round. Sometimes the going may be hard and the adult must be at hand to guide, but it must always be done for the fun of it. Throughout this book I will be referring again and again to the ALPS sequence.

The *least* important stage of learning is the last, that is, the use of abstract symbols to do sums. Most of our everyday calculations are done in our head anyway and not written down.

NOT A RACE

This venture into mathematics is not a *race*. Some of our pupils will never get beyond the nursery slopes where they can feel at home and understand what they are about. Nothing is gained by trying to push them up further from behind except bewilderment and misery. Other pupils, who can grasp ideas more quickly, may be raring to go on to explore fresh fields.

TRY ANOTHER WAY

There is no one right way of adding or subtracting; we probably all do it differently. Encourage your pupils to find different ways of solving problems themselves.

PUTTING KNOWLEDGE TO SOME USE

Ensure that mathematical experiences and activities are purposeful and not merely mock exercises carried out in the classroom. Respect your pupils and show them how, right from the start, they can put their knowledge to real use by helping you or their friends or themselves. Wherever possible, build up their independence and self esteem by giving them a part to play in real shopping, phoning, or catching a bus with real money. In this way they may make mistakes but will learn from them all the more quickly.

EVERYBODY'S PROVINCE

Number work should never just be the province of one person—the class teacher or parent—or only be tackled at set times during the day. Number and counting come into everything and everyone involved with a pupil (dinner lady, bus guide, cookery teacher, PE teacher) should have a good idea of each pupil's capability in this area. Then that pupil's ability can be put to use in a variety of settings, for example, he can count the chairs, find how many children are on the bus, follow a recipe, etc.

GAMES

Most of us play games at some time or other, and I have included many different games in this book. These games teach pupils to get along with one another socially both at home and in school. If they are games of chance they enable children to meet others on equal terms, and children with special needs will be as likely to win as their abler brothers and sisters. Numerical skills need constant practice, and through games children can practise their skills over and over again without getting bored.

RECORD SHEETS

Simple checklists in the form of record sheets are included at the back of this book. They are not meant as a curriculum, for true learning is a process which is still not fully understood. Children do not inevitably follow a logical sequence in their learning and may understand something 'difficult' before understanding something which we think is easier. For other children with learning difficulties, the jump from one item on the checklist to the next will be far too big a leap to make and we shall have to devise intermediate stages. The record sheets will enable us to check how much each individual pupil understands and remind us of other areas to tackle.

If this information can be shared by all those who come in contact with the pupil, then they will be in a position to ask appropriate questions.

THE DEVELOPMENTALLY YOUNG

Parents of young children may find this book useful as a preparation for school and I have included ways in which they can help their children long before they are ready for 'counting'. This section is also included to help parents and teachers of children who are chronologically much older but, because of their severe learning difficulties, are still developmentally very young. The activities described will apply to them also, especially if 'age-appropriate' materials are used.

A DISCLAIMER

For convenience sake, I have usually referred to the pupils in this book as 'he' and the parents and teachers as 'she'. These shorthand terms are intended to refer equally to either sex and, hopefully, will not be considered sexist.

Section One

THE NURSERY SLOPES

1 THE BACKGROUND TO ROTE COUNTING AND NUMERACY

We learn best when we do not realise that we are learning and teach best when we do not know that we are teaching.

The foundations of future learning are laid in infancy, often not deliberately but through the playful and natural interaction of parents and friends with the baby. Parents seem to be naturally programmed to adjust their interactions to the baby's developing needs and do not have to follow any special syllabus or checklist. Of course, some parents are better at this than others and some may feel inadequate with a child who is rather unresponsive and slow to develop. A more conscious effort may be needed in this case, but care should be taken that it does not impose extra demands on the child.

Normal rough and tumble play, peek-a-boo, pat-a-cake and baby talk are an ideal environment for early development (see the books *Let Me Play* and *Toys and Playthings* for further ideas). The baby will show by his eager anticipation and response that he is developing an appreciation of these games and absorbing their message.

Rhythmic games like pat-a-cake will give the baby the experience and 'feel' of 'threeness' long before he has any idea of number. Similarly, the two-fold rhythm will be absorbed as the grown-up intones 'tick-tock' in time with the clock. When 'This little pig went to market' is being played the baby is becoming gradually aware of the separate existence of his five toes. Do not underestimate these playful experiences or think they cannot be teaching anything because they are just 'having fun'. Actions and words repeated over and over again in a playful context will gradually lead to understanding.

ACTION SONGS
Action songs have long been a traditional feature of infancy and in many of these songs the child starts to hear the names of

numbers and become familiar with them. This familiarity with the names will make formal counting easier later on.

Here is an example of an early action rhyme with number names:

Round and round the garden
Like a teddy bear, *(run finger round palm)*
One step, two step, *(walk finger up arm)*
Tickle you under there. *(tickle under arm)*

Later many other rhymes and songs will be added to the repertoire. Here are a few:

One potato, two potato, three potato, four,
Five potato, six potato, seven potato more.

One, two, three, four, five,
Once I caught a fish alive.

One, two, three, four,
Mary at the cottage door,
Five, six, seven, eight,
Eating cherries off a plate.

Two little blackbirds *(hold up two forefingers)*
Sitting on a hill,
One called Jack *(wiggle right finger)*
and one called Jill. *(wiggle left finger)*
Fly away Jack! *(hide right finger at back of hand)*
Fly away Jill! *(hide left finger at back of hand)*
Come back Jack! *(bring back right finger)*
Come back Jill! *(bring back left finger)*

Five currant buns in a baker's shop, *(hold up five fingers)*

Round and fat with sugar on top. *(rub top of head)*

Along came a boy with a penny one day,
Bought a currant bun and took it away. *(bend little finger down)*

· Four currant buns in a baker's shop *(hold up four fingers)*

Round and fat with sugar on top

Along came a boy with a penny one day,
Bought a currant bun and took it away.
Three currant buns . . . *(and so on until all the fingers are
gone)*

The above rhymes all involve numbers less than ten. The following involve numbers over ten and should probably be recited mainly at school.

Ten green bottles hanging on a wall,
Ten green bottles hanging on a wall,
And if one green bottle should accidentally fall,
There'd be nine green bottles hanging on a wall.
Nine green bottles hanging on a wall . . . *(and so on until)*
There'd be no green bottles hanging on a wall.

Other rhymes such as 'This old man', 'One, two, buckle my shoe', and 'There were ten in the bed', can be found in the Ladybird series, *Learning with Traditional Rhymes* (the music is included for some of the rhymes). *Counting Rhymes*, obtainable from the Early Learning Centre, is also a useful source. Do not worry that your child will outgrow number rhymes and songs: some are appropriate at any age and even adults sing 'Ten green bottles' or 'The first day of Christmas'.

RHYTHM AND MUSIC

All rhythm and music has an essential numerical component, and perhaps that is why mathematical and musical ability often go together. Lucky is the child with musical parents who will sing and dance with him so that he absorbs the rhythm of the waltz or the polka. However, you do not have to be musical to vary your rhythm as you take a child for a walk, perhaps starting with a march, 'Left-right' or 'One-two, one-two', and so on. Then you might break into a run, 'One, two, three', or a skip, 'One, two, three and four'. Rhythmic counting as you push the swing is fun, and so is taking turns to beat a rhythm on a drum or saucepan or the cymbals, starting with a simple 'one, two' beat.

ROTE COUNTING

If a child is to learn to recite the number names in order he needs plenty of examples on which to model his performance.

You may have to repeat these experiences over and over again before he will begin to imitate you. When he does, do not put him off by correcting every mistake but accept his version at first. For instance, every time you go up and down stairs you could count the treads, sometimes pausing to see if he will join in. When in the street you could play the paving stones game, carefully stepping into the middle of each one as you count (avoiding the cracks where the dragons lurk!). This game can also be played indoors on a tiled floor or by stepping on each flower pattern on the carpet.

You could improvise on a rainy day by putting down old magazines or newspaper as stepping stones and striding from one to the next to avoid 'getting wet'. Older children are an asset here as they will probably enjoy these games and provide a good model for the younger or less mature child.

When out for a walk, let your child collect beautiful things such as leaves, nuts, acorns, feathers, conkers, etc. See how many he can find. Before he has learnt to count he can listen to you counting them out with pride as you point to each one: 'One, two, three, four, five, six, seven! You have seven, that's a lot!' Perhaps you could revive the old custom of making daisy chains and count the daisies as he collects them for you.

There are innumerable opportunities for counting as you carry out your daily chores around the house: counting the handkerchiefs when they have been ironed, counting the cups as you hang them up on their hooks, counting the chairs as you put them round the table, the forks and spoons as they are put away, and so on. Do not overload your child's memory by being too ambitious, just count the numbers up to three to start with and then up to five, and so on. Much repetition with different objects and situations will be needed before you are rewarded by hearing your child join in and start to repeat strings of numbers on his own.

With encouragement and praise, children usually enjoy counting in its own right just as they enjoy reciting a nursery rhyme. This should be a matter of pride even if, at first, the numbers are sometimes in the wrong order. Do not worry about this, it is a natural stage in their development which nearly all children pass through before getting them 'right'. Some children with good memories for rote learning may surprise you and be able to recite quite long sequences of numbers by rote. Do not be deceived by this ability for it does not necessarily mean that they have any idea of counting things out, or can tell you how many cherries there are on a plate. Counting by rote comes first and after this a child has much to learn before he can put this ability to any use, as you will see in Chapter 4, *'How Many Are There?'*

As a child matures, the ability to arrive at an understanding of mathematical or numerical concepts will depend a great deal on his or her early experiences.

Numerical concepts are built into the symmetry of both the natural and the man-made worlds around us and are there to be discovered. The symmetry of every flower or plant is based on numerical relationships—the arrangements of the leaves around the stem, the number of petals or seeds in a pod, for instance. Similarly, in the animal world, we find the regular number of limbs or of digits, eyes or ears. Even more fundamental is the rhythm of life itself—the rhythm of breathing, the beating of the heart, the rhythm of the days and of the seasons. Out of this world of nature come the rhythms that are characteristic of music and dance: the threefold rhythm of the waltz, and the fourfold rhythm of the march, for instance. All man-made objects, too, conceal numerical relationships of length, width and breadth, and are also numerically related to one another in sets—for example, pairs of shoes, numbers of fingers in gloves, panes of glass in the window, and so on.

The practical experience a child gains through his senses and through opportunities to handle objects, to experiment and discover numerical relationships for himself, is an essential preparation for more formal and abstract ideas of number.

Almost as soon as he is born a child is a natural explorer and experimenter and soon starts to discover some of the properties of the world around him. By mouthing objects he discovers that some are hard and some soft, and so on. Later he will experience various amounts, by spooning sugar on his cornflakes, for instance. Most importantly, many important discoveries are made through play, for in play a child is free to combine objects in many different ways, to discover their relative sizes and so on, without risk of failure, and to notice some seemingly irrelevant details.

How, then, can we help a child in this voluntary, self-initiated activity we call 'play'? The parent or teacher does not need to leave everything to chance but has a positive role in ensuring that a child has the maximum opportunity to learn through play. It is especially important today that teachers do assume this active role, for small children may easily be tempted away from active exploration by the lure of television, radio or tapes. There are several ways in which this kind of play can be fostered without making it any less spontaneous.

Play is said to be the work of a child and as such it must be respected. The adult who shows an interest in what the child is doing and is willing to become involved from time to time, will be at hand to make helpful suggestions without in any way trying to impose upon the situation. Above all it is up to the parent or teacher to provide suitable toys and playthings, at the appropriate time.

BRICKS

Elizabeth Newson (1979) and Matthews (1978) suggest that bricks are a very versatile plaything for all ages of children from twelve months to twelve years. Opportunities to play and construct with bricks enable them to experience many mathematical concepts at first hand. Matthews has pointed out that, by playing with bricks, children experience ordering and inclusion—for example, that three bricks are a part of a collection of five bricks; that one wall is longer than another but not as long as a third; that two bricks can be used to make the same height as one longer one. They will also begin to grasp the idea of conservation or invariance—for example, that four bricks are still four, however they may be arranged. These experiences are fundamental to a later understanding of mathematics.

He also suggests that if the mother or teacher takes an interest in the play and encourages talk, then a vocabulary of words such as big, high, low, far, near, long, deep, wide, tall, up and down will be acquired naturally in the course of the play.

Parents and teachers may find that a child shows little interest in a box of bricks. This may be because there are not enough bricks to build the castle or petrol station he has in mind and he becomes frustrated. Elizabeth Newson suggests that a hundred bricks with extra half bricks, pillars and other miscellaneous shapes would represent the absolute minimum requirement. She also suggests that the ordinary cube-shaped bricks which are readily available are not the ideal shape for building. Brick-shaped bricks 10cm × 5cm × 2.5cm) are ideal but are very expensive to buy even if they were commercially available. They will probably have to be cut to size by a machine joiner and then sanded and polished. This may represent a somewhat expensive outlay but will be well worth the money as the bricks will last for years and can be used by generations of children.

As the Newsons point out, it may not be enough just to provide the bricks: often the parent or teacher will have to get down on the floor and demonstrate possibilities by building bridges, trains or towers. She or he will also need to be tolerant: to insist that everything is cleared away after each playtime can be most frustrating for the budding architect. The parent or teacher should also accept whatever the child wishes to do with the bricks. Instead of building with them he or she may use them in an imaginative game and pretend they are sandwiches, or the younger child may experiment with banging two bricks together. The parent who enters into the spirit of the game, whatever it is, and is willing to follow the child's lead, is in a position to make suggestions which further the play, so long as this is done sensitively.

3 BEFORE COUNTING

Before a child can be expected to follow a command such as 'Give me a pencil' or 'Fetch two pencils', he must be able to recognise a pencil by use, even though no two pencils look exactly alike. That is to say, he must recognise the essential similarities of all pencils as well as being able to spot the differences. This ability to sort out essential similarities in spite of differences does not usually have to be taught but does need the provision of a variety of experiences and the help of a supportive adult. You can generally tell whether a child is able to recognise objects by their use by listening to him talking or by watching him at play. If he recognises or names a 'cup' which is a different shape or colour from his own cup, can find a picture of a cup in a book or magazine if asked, or 'pretends' to drink from a toy cup, to comb his hair with a toy comb or to take a bite out of a picture of an apple, he is well on the way to spotting essential similarities and differences between objects.

However, this recognition by use needs to be further encouraged with a variety of different pictures and toys and by an adult who is willing to join in the pretence. The next step after this will be the gradual recognition of other common attributes of objects: they may be round or soft or smooth or prickly. Practice in sorting and matching will accelerate this process.

When a child begins to count it may be obvious that he has not yet realised that numbers must follow one another in a given order. Random counting of one, six, two, three, five will not do. A child who has experience of ordering other things, like putting different-sized rings in order on a stack, should have less difficulty here.

In this chapter, various games and activities will be described which will help to nurture the concepts which precede the understanding of number and the ability to count.

As a child develops new concepts we can help him by giving him the words with which to express them. A child enlarges his vocabulary and discovers the meaning of new words by hearing the same words used over and over again in new contexts, as the adult makes a natural commentary on ongoing events. The meaning will be clearest if the commentary is directed towards whatever is holding the child's attention at a given moment. In this way understanding will develop naturally and flexibly, as a gradual process, and a child's own use of words will reflect this. His current use of words should be accepted so long as his meaning is clear: as his understanding grows his vocabulary will become more conventional.

PRACTICAL ACTIVITIES

Sorting
In order to be able to sort out a collection of objects you have to be able to spot their similarities and differences. There is no need for expensive apparatus to encourage sorting: materials around the house or in the garden or park can all be used for this practice.

APPARATUS

Containers
Margarine cartons, plant-pot saucers, tin lids, bowls, etc.

Contents
In the house: buttons, cotton reels, dried beans, pencils, india rubbers, paper fasteners, large beads, squares of material, nuts, etc.
In the kitchen: potatoes, oranges, apples, nutmegs, spoons, forks.
Toys: balls, dinky cars, miniature animals, doll's furniture, plates, cups and cutlery, pictures (cut from catalogues).
Out of doors: leaves, shells, flowers, pebbles, acorns, conkers, sticks, etc.

PROCEDURE

Stage one
Provide two containers and two categories of objects which are quite dissimilar—for example, buttons and pencils. Mix them up together and place one button in one container and one pencil in the other as a starter, then encourage the child to sort out the rest.

Stage two
Gradually increase the number of categories, first to three, then four, and so on, *or* use some of the original contents and try sorting them by a different attribute, such as colour, size, etc.—yellow buttons in here, blue buttons in there—*or* let the child sort out the things he likes from those he does not like, *or* John's toys from Bill's toys.

Stage three
Sort out miniature objects which do not look alike but have the same use or belong to the same category of objects (chairs in here, mats in there; fruit in here, vegetables in there; animals in here, plants in there). A child can often sort out things which go together before he knows their collective names—for example, animals, furniture, vehicles, etc.

You can make sorting more complex by sorting the same objects first by use—all the things we eat—and then by another attribute—all the red ones.

It is also important when undertaking a sorting task to be able to realise negative attributes. When a child has sorted out a set of red objects or blue objects, let him resort and put in one set all the objects which are *not* red or *not* blue. Similarly, he could sort out things we *do not* eat.

FIND ANOTHER
This is a good game to play with one or two children, especially when outside. The teacher holds up an object, for example a leaf, and the children have to look round and find another like it. This can become a race. The child's choice of object may not be what the teacher expected but you should accept their choice so long as it makes sense—for example, instead of bringing a leaf a child may bring an acorn (because they are both green).

RECOGNITION BY ATTRIBUTES

A selection of picture cards is laid face up on the table. The leader asks, 'Which one drinks milk?' or, 'Which do we sleep in?' or, 'Which one is red?' or, 'Which has four legs?' The players see who can be first to point to the right card which they then keep. The leader should vary the questions at a subsequent session so as to keep the children on their toes.

GAMES WITH PEOPLE

In school try sorting out all the boys and all the girls. Play a game and get the pupils to stand up when you call out, 'All those in blue,' or, 'All with black shoes,' or, 'Those wearing a skirt.'

VOCABULARY

By playing these games the players should begin to grasp the meaning of many attribute words such as round, square, shiny, fat, thin, red, blue, green and black.

This ability to sort into groups or *sets* is fundamental to the understanding of modern mathematics and it is a good idea to introduce the word 'set' when playing these sorting games: a *set* of chairs or a *set* of cups or fruit.

COLLECTIONS

Practice in sorting can lead to the making of many different collections. Teachers could mount a display of all the leaves the class has collected or all the red things they can find in the garden, or make a collection of pictures of clothes or furniture, first sorted and then suitably displayed.

EDUCATIONAL TOYS

There are many educational toys on the market designed to help with the sorting of shapes, colours, etc. Abbatt and Galt make shape posting boxes and Willis Toys make a clipper cart with rods.

Matching or Pairing

Even before they can count, children can collect the right number of milk bottles, straws, pencils, chairs, etc. for each member of the class to have one. This they can do by matching each pupil with an object—one for you and one for you, and so on. This is called one-to-one correspondence and it is a concept which develops with maturity and experience. Some children with learning difficulties may need extra help in this area; they may be deceived by what their eyes tell them. For instance, six milk bottles grouped close together may not *look* enough for six children sitting apart. Practice in matching or pairing them one-to-one will help these chldren to get it right.

Let your pupils have *real* opportunities to experiment and find out about one-to-one correspondence. For instance, give them the job of putting the chairs round the table ready for a meal. In this way they will soon discover if they have the wrong number by having no place to sit or too many empty chairs. Do not be in a hurry to intervene but let them sort it out. Similarly, pupils can take it in turns to give round the milk, straws, pencils or books. If pupils are able to recognise the printed names of their classmates they can prepare the right number beforehand by matching a name with each milk bottle. They can then match each bottle with a straw.

Another help for pupils who cannot recognise printed names by sight is to invest in a collection of individual class photographs which they can use. Some pupils may be able to remember the names of all the pupils in the class and collect a bottle for each name, not forgetting themselves. Tidying up the empty bottles and putting them into crates, or the pencils into pencil holders, or the cups on their hooks, is all good practice in one-to-one correspondence. So is matching buttons to holes when doing up a coat or using a practice button board. Such real experiences are more effective than artificial exercises because pupils can see the result of getting it wrong. Extra practice can be given by giving the pupil a model and getting him to match the beads and thread them in the same order.

MATCHING OR PAIRING GAMES

Play a game either with one pupil or with a group by holding up an object and seeing if they can find something that goes with it—cup and saucer, table and chair, or another red object.

Make or buy a set of pairs of cards which are not identical but can be used for pairing, for example, two different chairs, two animals, two houses, two brushes, etc. (These could be cut from catalogues and mounted on cards.) These cards can be used for a number of different matching games.

1 *Find another.* The cards are laid face up on the table or spread on the furniture around the room. One card is held up and the game is for the pupils to find its pair.

2 *Snap.* This is played in the usual way but before saying 'Snap' you have to spot that the cards are a pair although they are not identical.

3 *Pairs or pelmanism.* The cards are laid face down on the table. Each player has to turn up two cards without changing their position on the table. If these cards go together (for example, are both birds or fruit), then the player keeps them. If not, he turns them face down again and the next player has his turn.

EDUCATIONAL TOYS
Many early educational toys give practice in matching and pairing. For instance, the wooden boats with peg people to fit in the holes, or toys for buttoning into button holes. Many of these toys are stocked by the Early Learning Centres found in most big towns. Play Matters (The Toy Libraries Association) publish an excellent *Good Toy Guide* which describes the toys and their uses, together with names and addresses of suppliers. For older pupils these toys may be a little babyish and household objects would be more age appropriate. Eggs can be put into egg boxes or egg cups (ping pong balls may be substituted), pegs can be used for hanging handkerchiefs out to dry, and so on.

VOCABULARY
In the course of these jobs and games the pupils will begin to grasp the meaning of words like 'more', 'less', 'the same', 'too many', 'too few', 'enough', etc.

Putting in order
Numeracy is primarily concerned with the ordering of the universe. This may be by position, size, height, weight, distance or speed. Pupils are often expected to get into a line when

moving from place to place and in this way they gradually appreciate the meaning of first and last. Perhaps they can also gain an idea of ordering by height, for example, the tallest first and then the next tallest, and so on.

Steps are an obvious example of ordering, and the idea of higher or lower can be experienced by trying your skill at jumping off. Towers built by different children can be compared for height. Stacking toys also provide practice in ordering, either sets of stacks or single stacks with rings of graded sizes. (Most educational toy shops stock a selection of ring stacks and nesting beakers. Brio toys make a nice wooden ring pyramid.)

For the young, the story of *Goldilocks and the Three Bears*, illustrated with pictures or toys, provides a good introduction to comparative sizes. Pupils' attention can also be regularly drawn to ordering in time, with comments from the teacher as to who was first to arrive in the morning or to be ready for PE. Similarly, talk about the ages of pupils gives an idea of ordering—who is the oldest in the class and who is the youngest, or whether Peter is older or younger than Henry. Talk could also centre around the steps made of building bricks.

It must be remembered that ordering is fundamental to counting. We cannot count accurately in a random order, as many children will start off by doing, for example, three, four, seven. When trying to count out objects it is important to put them in some kind of order so that we know where we started and do not count any twice or miss any of them. There are many ways of giving practice in ordering: for instance, when threading beads you could start the pupil off by threading in a simple pattern, such as one round bead and one square one, and let the pupil continue. The telling of daily news gives the pupils the idea of ordering events in time and starting with getting up and then dressing, and so on.

EDUCATIONAL TOYS
Ring pyramids, wooden Russian dolls, building beakers.

VOCABULARY
With constant practice in ordering the pupils will begin to add new words to their vocabulary: first, last, bottom, top, big,

bigger, biggest, tall, taller, tallest, short, shorter, shortest, old, older, oldest, young, younger, youngest, small, smaller, smallest, in front of, between, behind, etc.

Invariance

Another concept that children have to learn is called the 'invariance of number': that is, that five bottles will still be five, however they are arranged, mixed up or moved around. Very young children may not be aware of the fact that when you post two bricks in a box, two will come out. Even when children are able to count out a number of objects, they may feel that they must count them again if someone muddles them up. Games with posting boxes are a good way of helping children to acquire the idea of invariance of objects. Toys for the Handicapped (TFH) supply an excellent posting box for such games, with an inbuilt reinforcement. It is called the One Armed Bandit Box and although rather expensive, is strong and versatile and well worth the money.

VOCABULARY
Still the same, no more, no less, in and out.

4 HOW MANY ARE THERE?

The ability to recite the number names in the correct order is something we have already introduced in Chapter 1. It is essential to be able to do this before we can answer the question, 'How many sweets are there in the box?' or, 'How many children have arrived?' However, this mechanical counting is not all we need in order to answer these questions correctly. It is quite possible for a child to be able to recite a long string of numbers correctly (or count up to twenty, say) and still be unable to count out a number of objects without mistakes. Many children with learning difficulties seem to take a very long time to master this skill. As an adult to whom counting is second nature, it is easy to become impatient with them unless we try to put ourselves in the child's place and realise how much is involved.

In the previous chapter we discussed the various skills a child will need to have developed before he can be expected to count out a pile of coins accurately or say how many fingers you are holding up. These included an ability to recognise objects by use, sort objects into sets or groups, arrange objects in a logical order, one-to-one correspondence or pairing, and invariance of objects. To this must be added the ability to remember the number names in the right order.

We shall illustrate this by seeing what skills are involved in finding how many cows there are in a toy farm. Before he can arrive at a correct answer a child has to do the following:

* recognise the animals which fit the description 'cow' and distinguish them from those which do not (*recognition by use*)
* sort the animals into two sets: cows and not cows (*sorting*)
* be able to recite as many number names in order as there are cows (*rote counting*)
* pair each cow with a number name without missing any out or counting any twice (*pairing*)

* stop counting once the last cow has been named: this number tells you how many there are in the set (*invariance*).
NOTE. It is easy for a child to confuse ordinal and cardinal numbers. The last cow to be touched when counting in order was the fourth (ordinal number), but the cardinal number, four, tells you how many there are in the group and does not depend on the order in which you count them.

I suggest that you set your pupils this task with just a few animals and observe at which stage they go wrong. (If a pupil completes the task accurately you could increase the number of animals.)

A pupil who adds sheep or pigs to his group of cows may have difficulty in recognising things that are *not* cows by their negative attributes, an important aspect of sorting.

A pupil may try to count the cows in a higgledy-piggledy fashion, missing some out or counting some twice: further practice in ordering would be appropriate.

A pupil may fail to say the number names in the right order—for example, one, two, four, three—and will need more practice in this.

A common mistake is a failure to match or pair the number names with the objects, failing to touch each object as it is counted and counting too fast and getting too high a total, or leaving some out and getting the total too low.

Many pupils may not realise that the last number uttered tells you how many there are in the group and is not the number name of that particular cow.

PRACTICAL ACTIVITIES FROM ONE TO FIVE
In the rest of this chapter we are going to suggest a number of practical activities and games which will help your pupils to answer the question 'How many are there?' without help. At first it is best to confine these games and activities to small numbers, perhaps one to five. A child who can count mechanically up to ten, twenty or beyond will often make mistakes when counting out a set of objects. Counting out ten objects is far harder and requires a greater attention span than counting out five. It is best not to be too ambitious but to start with small numbers and, when the pupil is ready, the same games can be played and the size of the sets increased.

THE THREENESS OF THREE

The numbers two, three or four are names given to a very abstract concept. We can have three pigs, three balls or three people and these things have nothing in common individually: the threeness applies only to the size of the group or set. A child may have difficulty in grasping this idea until he has had enough experience with a large variety of sets of objects.

More sorting games will be a help. This time you need to prepare the objects to be sorted. Gather together two of each of a variety of objects and as many containers as there are kinds of objects. Mix up the objects together on the table and then ask the child to sort them out—for example, to sort out the animals and put them into one container and the birds in another and so on. When he has sorted them correctly, get him to count the number in each container—for example one, two (two animals), one, two (two birds) and so on. Point out that there are *two* in each container. Give plenty of practice with the number two before going on to three in each set, or four or five. If your child begins to know how many there are without having to count them every time, then you are winning as he is now recognising the threeness of three or the conservation of number.

Some children can recognise three objects when they are arranged in one particular pattern but fail to recognise that they are the same number when the pattern differs. Philip and Tacey sell some *Conservation of Number Snap Cards*. Pairs of cards have the same number of pips arranged in different patterns. When matching pairs turn up, the players call out 'five' or 'two' instead of 'snap'.

FROM THE WHOLE TO THE PARTS

It may sound rather far fetched to suggest that the way in which we first introduce children to number may have an effect upon their future moral outlook. Certainly, most people agree that we live in an acquisitive society whose goals are often getting more and more. Recently there have been signs of a reaction towards a more holistic approach to life. Perhaps a new approach to numeracy which encourages giving rather than getting could be a healthy idea which is less threatening to the child.

For this approach, start with a familiar object, an apple or a cake. The problem for the teacher and child is that there is only one apple and both of them would enjoy a bite. If the apple is then cut in half the child can share it with his mother or teacher and appreciate the fact that *two* pieces can come from *one* apple. If there are other children in the group the apple could be cut in *four* and the segments passed round. There are many other examples: a whole bar of chocolate can be broken into bits, a whole box of crayons can contain a number of crayons to share around.

Useful practice in counting can come from starting with the whole and sharing out the parts.

Active games
To associate counting and numeracy with the classroom only is a mistake. It is important in this context to involve the whole child in active movement so that he absorbs numerical concepts in his bones. A balance can be achieved by interspersing these activities with quieter table games.

STEPPING STONES

In the context of rote counting in Chapter 1, I suggested that you seize every opportunity to count the paving stones when out for a walk, or to count the steps when coming in. I also suggested you could make stepping stones of old magazines or papers on the living room or classroom floor. At that stage *you* were doing most of the counting, with your child gradually joining in more and more. Now that he is familiar with these games he can play them on his own or with a group of children. However, now more than rote counting is involved. I suggest that you start with just a few stepping stones and help him to pair each number with just one step and to stop counting when he has reached the last 'stone' and tell you how many stones there were altogether.

Pin down two tapes to show the width of the river. Let him stand on the near bank and step onto the first stone, saying 'one', and then onto the next saying 'two', and the last saying 'three'. Ask him to tell you how many stones there are. Make it all into a game—if his foot touches the 'water' or he makes a mistake in counting, then the 'shark' will get him and he will have to start again. When he is able to cope well with three stones, increase the number gradually. Perhaps you could make it harder by making him stop in the middle of the river and then continue counting on. You could call out STOP at different points on his journey. Then you could see whether he is able to return over the stones counting in reverse: 'Five, four, three, two, one and home!' It is a good idea to leave the stones down so that he can practise on his own or watch other children having a go.

FORMING GROUPS

A good game for a class of children in the hall is to get them running around (to music ideally) and when the music stops and the teacher calls out a number from one to five (for example, *three*), the children have to get into groups of three and the odd ones out sit down.

MUSICAL CHAIRS

This is a familiar game and can involve a great deal of counting and pairing as well as understanding terms like 'away', 'less', 'too many' and 'too few'. It is probably best to start with a small group of children, perhaps four or five. Ask each pupil to bring his chair into a row in the middle of the room and sit on it. Ask each pupil in turn to tell you how many children there are and then how many chairs. Note whether they know that if there are five children there will be five chairs (conservation of number) or whether they start counting the chairs separately. Get every other child to turn his chair round to face the other way. Everyone stands up and the teacher takes away a chair, commenting as she does so. The music starts and the children walk or run around the chairs. When the music stops they sit down on the nearest chair and the pupil without a chair is *out*. Then another chair is taken away and so on.

Table games

These are devised for one or more players. The aim is to get the pupils to play together independently and perhaps to play the games also at home. Some children with learning difficulties may have become so used to being directed individually by a parent or teacher in a one-to-one situation that this is how the games will have to be introduced until the pupils are very familiar with the rules and ready to play with each other. The initial work is well worth the effort as, once the pupils are able to play together, the teacher is free to give her undivided attention to others who need it.

Some games may require special apparatus, but many can be played with junk material at little or no cost.

EGG SORTING

Apparatus
One egg box for each player, six ping pong balls for each player, a pack of cards.
Note: only the lower denominations of cards are used for this game that is, one (ace), two and three.

The cards are shuffled and the pack is placed face down on the table. In front of each player is an empty egg box. All the eggs(balls) are placed in a container in the middle of the table.

To play
Each player in turn picks the top card of the pack and counts the pips and places that number of eggs in his box. The card is then placed underneath the rest of the pack. The first player to fill his box wins. The last card must equal the number of places left in his box for him to go; if the last card exceeds that number he must miss a turn. Higher denomination cards can gradually be added to the pack, or alternatively a dice can be used in the place of cards.

STACKING THE RINGS

Apparatus
A ring stack for each player holding just ten rings.
    (A handy man or woman with a brace and bit and some offcuts of wood and dowelling could make these. The rings do not have to be round!)
A set of programmed dice made from small wooden bricks with adhesive spots on the faces. A beginner's dice should have only one or two or three spots on each face. One face is left blank, and if this face turns up the player must miss a turn. Alternatively playing cards can be used as above.

To play
All the rings are placed in the middle of the table. Each player throws the dice in turn, counts the number of spots on the face and threads that number of rings on the stack. If the last throw exceeds the number required to fill the stack the player must miss a turn and try again when his turn comes round. This is important, as players begin to realise the number needed to complete their stack if, for instance, they already have seven rings on the stack. This game teaches the number bonds of ten.

RACE GAME
There are many race games on the market and all give practice in counting, but most of them are too difficult at this stage and a DIY version is suggested.

Materials
Cardboard (white), felt-tipped pen, counters, dice (as above) or playing cards, adhesive stars.

To make
Cut out strips of white card 30 cms (12 ins) long by 2.5 cms (1 in) wide and mark then into 2.5 cm squares with a felt-tipped pen. Stick a coloured star into the middle of the last square to mark the winning post.

To play
Each player is provided with a board and coloured counter. Players take turns to throw the dice or turn up a card and then move their counter the appropriate number of squares along the board. The one to reach the star first wins. In the book *Let's Join In*, published by Souvenir Press in their Human Horizons series, you will find instructions for making a programmed series of race games leading to the commercial games like Snakes and Ladders.

FLOUNDERING
Floundering is an excellent commercial game marketed by Spears, and in *Let's Join In* you will find suggestions for adapting this game for beginners. Similar commercial games are: Create-a-Clown (Ravensburg) and Animal Sixes (Galt). These, too, may need simplifying for the beginner.

PAIRS OR PELMANISM

Materials
A pack of playing cards. Only two suits are used for this game and only the lower denominations (one to five).

To play
Shuffle the cards and spread them out face down on the table. Each player turns up two cards and if they match he keeps them. Players should be encouraged to count the number of pips on each card they turn up and, if they differ, they must be turned back again. This is not only a good counting and number recognition game but also a test of memory and is popular with children who are often better than adults at remembering where the cards were.

DOMINOES

Apparatus
A set of number dominoes played in the usual way. Pupils who cannot yet count out the higher denominations can match them by eye but should check the rest by counting.

Further practice in conservation
If your pupils have to count anew every time the positioning of a group of numbers is changed, they are not yet conserving and need more practice.

USING A MONEY BOX
Accustom the pupils or children at home to use a money box for saving. Let them post a small number of coins in the box, counting them one at a time as they go in. Ask how many have gone in. If a child can tell you, then he is conserving. Open the box and ask if he knows how many you can take out; if he does not, let him check by counting again.

POSTING BOXES
A similar game can be played with a simple posting box, either with one child or with a group. Objects are posted into the box and counted one by one as they go in. Which of the pupils can tell you how many there are in the box without having to count again when they are turned out?

This game is best introduced in a one-to-one situation and can then be played by a group taking turns to decide how many objects to post and then counting them as they go in. The rest of the group take turns to guess how many objects are in the box and check who is right by turning them out and counting them.

An excellent (but expensive) posting box can be bought from Toys for the Handicapped (TFH), which ejects the contents of the box onto the table when the handle is pressed. This is very popular, and to keep up the interest, be ready to improvise new games with this box. For instance, the pupils, instead of counting, might try to remember which objects have gone into the box, for example, a ball, a cat and a cotton reel. Before the contents are ejected and checked they could work out in their heads the number of things to come out. It is quite acceptable to use your fingers.

If funds will not run to the 'One Armed Bandit Post Box' described above, then a simple upside-down cardboard box with a hole in the bottom can suffice, so long as the drama of lifting the box and revealing the contents is sustained!

Counting in other lessons and situations
Like anyone else, children need plenty of practice in counting, otherwise they get rusty. They can get this practice in many different situations both at home and in school, with a bit of encouragement from the grown-ups. However, appropriate practice will not be given unless parents, teachers and ancillary staff are aware of the level of a child's competence. A simple checklist such as the one at the back of this book could be completed for each child and be available to everybody for reference.

DAILY LIVING SKILLS
Most special schools set great store by fostering skills needed for daily living and these sessions provide pupils with many opportunities to put their counting ability to some use. It is important that these opportunities are not missed as they will enable the pupil to do things himself if given the chance.

The opportunities are endless and only a few will be described in this section. The rest is up to you!

REMEMBER
Keep the task well within the pupil's level of ability so that he can carry it out independently with the minimum of adult direction. Wherever possible allow him time to solve his own problems given your interest and encouragement.

Putting out and clearing away
Pupils who have hitherto helped to give out the milk at break time by matching or pairing will now be able to count the number of pupils and bring the right number of bottles, beakers or straws. If the milk for the whole class is too much to deal with at that stage, they could put the milk out table by table; different pupils could be responsible for different tables. If they get it wrong let them correct themselves. At snacktime they could be responsible for putting the right number of chairs around the tables. Perhaps a cake will have to be cut up and shared round. Washing up the beakers and putting them away gives added practice in one-to-one correspondence.

Giving out pencils, books and letters can also be the responsibility of some of the pupils who can check that they have given out the right number by counting. At home setting the table at meal times gives practice in counting out the right number of place mats, plates, knives, forks, spoons and napkins, etc.

Cookery
Pupils often start off their cookery curriculum by learning to make drinks, either cold drinks or hot drinks for the class. Let *them* be responsible for counting the number of people wanting drinks, counting out the right number of beakers and the right number of spoonfuls of sugar or coffee or bags of tea. Even those pupils who cannot yet be trusted with a kettle can help in the early preparations of a hot drink.

PICTURE RECIPES
Pupils will be much more independent if they learn to follow some kind of recipe when they have reached the stage of making cakes, for instance.

A chart on the wall or individual sheets can show how many spoonfuls of sugar, cupfuls of flour, segments of fat or eggs are

needed for the recipe and each pupil will be able to look at the
pictures and assemble the right amounts. Let them discuss how
many paper cases to get ready and how many cherries they will
need to put on the top of each cake. James Hargreaves, in
Cookery for Handicapped People (Souvenir Press), warns
parents and teachers not to underestimate a handicapped
child, for encouragement towards responsibility and independence is the only way ever to achieve it.

In the art lesson
When friezes are made with handprints and discussed after-
wards, attention can be drawn to the number of hands in the
print, or the number of children who have made prints, or the
number of fingers in one pupil's handprint. In this case the
counting does not need to be laboured but nevertheless it can
usefully come in incidentally. When children are making
potato prints their efforts are often very haphazard to begin
with. Perhaps you could suggest that they make four prints in
each row or five in a row.

Further experience of ordering can come from patterns
made with two shapes alternating, and so on. Corks make good
printing blocks either whole or cut in half, and so do carrots cut
across.

Section Two

COUNTING FROM ONE TO TEN

5 ORDINAL NUMBERS

So far most of this book has been concerned with cardinal numbers which are the numbers that tell how many there are in a group, for example, five. Ordinal numbers, on the other hand, indicate the order of placement within the group, for example, fifth. There would be less confusion if we always distinguished between ordinal and cardinal numbers, for example, between fourth and four, seventh and seven, etc. The confusion may arise from the fact that cardinal numbers are sometimes used loosely to indicate placement in an ordered array. When asked how we did in a competition we may answer, 'I was number five,' instead of saying, 'I came fifth.' This does not cause confusion in later life but it may confuse a child learning to count. Here is a little test to see if you can easily spot which are ordinal and which are cardinal numbers in the following:

a   His address is 4, Ash Grove, Bolton.
b   I do not want many potatoes, 2 will be plenty.
c   Turn to page 7 in your reading book.
d   There will be 8 at the party.
e   Johnny is 8 today.

Turn to the end of this chapter to see whether you got them all right.

A child needs some time to sort all this out. He may be so used to counting the fingers on one hand in the same order—one, two, three, four, five, ending with the thumb— that he may link each number with a particular finger, five being the thumb and not the fifth digit on his hand. Look out for signs of this confusion of cardinal and ordinal numbers if a child's answers appear 'wrong' to you. He needs plenty of practice before he can understand that the number 'five' is not just the number of the thumb but relates to the size of the whole group.

It is important to spot these signs of misunderstanding as they can be serious. For instance, a young person who has been told to catch the number five bus from the stop may let four go past and get onto the next bus which will not be the number five at all.

PRACTICE WITH ORDINAL NUMBERS

First and last

As an introduction to the idea of ordinal placement, it is important that the pupils understand 'first' and 'last' in a variety of situations. Some time each day the pupils will probably line up to change classes or to be given their letters for home. Comment on who is first or last in the line today. See if they can tell you who is first and then suggest a change in the order: 'Let Joe be first in the line today, and Lisa can be last.' See if they can change the order without your help. Then choose one of the pupils to tell you who is first today and who is last. Choose a different pupil each time.

Remember to use the words first and last in other situations, not only first and last in space but also in time: 'See who can be the first to get dressed to go out.' Make sure that the pupils can tell you who was first and who was last.

When the pupils are stringing beads, see if they can tell you the colour of the first bead in the string, or ask them to thread a yellow bead first. You could play a game with toy animals, perhaps lining them up behind a screen and then guessing which was first and which was last in the line. Let the pupils take turns with just a few animals at first. Gradually introduce second and then third into the game. Vary the game by lining up the animals and see who can tell you which animal is second in the line. You must all view the line from the same side. You could then 'steal' one when they are looking the other way and ask which has gone. They may *name* the animal; accept this answer and then ask, 'Was the pig first or second in the line?'

Story time

It is useful to know ordinal numbers in order to identify houses in the street. Before expecting the pupils to put this skill to use outside and find the houses, let them get used to the idea imaginatively in a story, with visual aids.

Visual aids

Prepare a frieze of a row of houses and cut round the doors so that they open when flapped back. Use polaroid photos of each member of the class on a stand. Let them choose their own houses in the row and stand their photo in front of the door.

The teacher chooses a different house each day for the story. She begins by reminding the pupils about the order of the houses: 'This is the first house, the second house and so on . . . Can you find the third house? John lives in the third house, so today's story is about John.'

The teacher then tells a short story about John. The next time she might let one of the pupils tell the story: whoever lives in the fifth house can tell his story, and so on. Another time you might choose a different set of householders depending upon current interests, for example, *Coronation Street* characters, or *EastEnders*, perhaps. When the pupils are familiar with the ordinal numbers of a row of five or six, you could print the numbers on the house doors to aid the recognition of numerals.

Table games

To give individual practice in ordinal numbers.

Materials

Each pupil has a strip of paper marked out in largish squares and a box of crayons or set of coloured pencils. They have to listen carefully as the teacher gives instructions: 'Colour the first square blue . . . colour the fourth square blue,' and so on. If they have five squares on their strip and do not yet know the word 'fifth', they can be asked to colour the *last* square green. You can test the pupil's ability by varying your instructions, for example: 'Find the square next to the blue square and colour it brown.' For pupils who are uncertain of the names of colours you could hold up a crayon and say, 'Colour the second square this colour.'

VOCABULARY

First, last, before, after, between, in front of, behind, next, second, third, fourth, fifth, sixth, seventh, eighth, ninth, straight line, left, right.

Answers to the questions on p. 40
    a   ordinal
    b   cardinal
    c   ordinal
    d   cardinal
    e   cardinal

Alan Graham has written a useful guide for parents of young children called *Help Your Child with Maths*. In this he reminds parents that at some stage a child must learn to recognise and draw the symbols we use to represent numbers, that is, 1,2,3,4,5,6,7,8,9 and so on. These are called numerals. Alan Graham advises parents to resist the urge to teach this important skill in the preschool years. He suggests that there is much to learn by physical exploration (handling bricks, conkers, pebbles, bottle tops, etc.) and by talking about them, collecting and sorting, counting and comparing, before these complicated symbols should be introduced. He goes on to suggest that doing and saying needs plenty of practice before the introduction of the reading and writing of numerals.

In this book we have adopted the same philosophy and given the name ALPS to remind parents and teachers of the order in which learning takes place. ALPS stands for the following:

A   ACTIVE physical exploration and handling of objects.
L   LANGUAGE—the natural language which accompanies active exploration and forms a commentary on it, that is, adults and children talk about what they are doing.
P   PICTURES—active experiences can be recalled and recorded in picture form or as rebuses.
S   SYMBOLS—the recognition of numerals and other mathematical symbols such as plus and minus, and the ability to manipulate them in *sums*.

Although some pupils with learning difficulties will eventually reach the summit of the ALPS, teachers and parents should not to be in a hurry to reach this stage. Calculations can be carried out without the use of numerals and mathematical symbols, especially if pictures or rebuses are used, for example, numbers of objects can be represented by patterns of dots quite early on. Packs of playing cards with the picture cards removed can be used for number recognition, for instance. They can be used as flash cards, using only the lower denominations (one to three) at first. Rules of addition, subtraction, multiplication and division can all be learnt using these cards. So nothing is to be lost by delaying the introduction of numerals, especially when your pupils have difficulty in learning anyway.

TRY THIS EXERCISE
This exercise will help you to appreciate the complexity of dealing with numerals if you are a child. Imagine that instead of writing 1,2,3,4,5,6,7,8,9, we were to use letters of the alphabet for the numbers one to nine: a,b,c,d,e,f,g,h,i. Can you add c and g quickly? Or a and i? Can you write 49 or 134, or multiply d by h, or say how many 'diea' is? This is not as difficult a task as the ones we set our pupils, but it is hard enough.

Perhaps it will persuade you to delay the introduction of numerals for a while.

Incidental learning
However, before the formal teaching of 'reading' and 'writing' numerals begins there will be some incidental learning taking place. Boys and girls will see written numerals about them in the environment. Some may begin to ask questions: 'What does that (No. 5) say?' And of course, if they do, they should be told. The story of the houses which we suggested in Chapter 5 will provide some incidental learning of this kind.

Preparation for forming numerals
Practice in pattern making can be a useful preparation for forming figures correctly later on. Most children form some numerals back to front or upside down at first. This can become a habit, and so pupils are often given the somewhat monotonous task of tracing round figures. All numerals are formed from a combination of circles, vertical lines, horizontal lines, and curves. Pattern making gives practice in forming these freehand. Developmentally children are able to copy a circle and vertical and horizontal lines before being able to form oblique lines and curves accurately.

FIRST PATTERNS

Materials

These should be varied to add to the interest. Large brushes, poster paint, sugar paper and an easel can be used, or crayons with smaller sheets of paper on a table, or felt-tipped pens, or even a stick for scratching patterns in the sand.

The first pattern might be rows of circles:

O O O O O O O O

Then a pattern can be made with circles and vertical lines:

O | O | O | O | O | O

Then perhaps a row of crosses followed by crosses and circles:

+ + + + + O + O + O

Then oblique lines can be introduced in different patterns:

∧ ∧ ∧ ∧ ∧   X X X X X

The teacher or parent will probably have to start the row or draw a complete row for the child to copy underneath. Although, at some point, it is useful to introduce the words 'circle', 'cross' and 'straight line', for the young child, or for any child who is unfamiliar with these terms, it is best to use your imagination and suggest making a row of balloons or balls or plates. The second pattern might be a plate and a knife ready for dinner and, of course, the crosses can be kisses and can be practised on the bottom of letters to friends and family.

SYMMETRY

The concept of symmetry is an underlying mathematical concept. The following patterns give a pupil practice in drawing symmetrical shapes and also lead to the ability to form numerals correctly.

Start by the teacher drawing half of a symmetrical shape and letting the pupil complete it, for example, a pear shape:

teacher's half   the pupil adds his half freehand to make   the complete pear.

Or an apple on a plate leads directly to the pupil being able to draw the numeral 2:

teacher's half   the pupil adds his half freehand to make   apple on a plate. Cut in half makes 2.

Other numbers can be introduced in the form of symmetrical patterns, for example:

teacher's half   with pupil's half   cut in half.

If numbers are introduced in this way, the pupil learns to form them correctly both the right way round and the right way up.

Once a pupil is able to complete these patterns fairly accurately, he could make a pattern by completing a row of 2s, for instance.

It is important that he gets into the habit of starting his numerals at the correct point. A dot on each numeral to copy indicates where to begin: The numerals 1,2,3,6,7,8 and 9 are all

2 1 3 6 7 8 9

formed without taking the pencil off the paper but 4 and 5 are formed with two pencil strokes, thus:

(the dot marks the beginning of each stroke)

4 5

LDA market a useful aid to writing numerals called 'rol'n write numbers'.

THE RECOGNITION OF NUMERALS

A number strip could be hung on the wall with the first three

numerals printed on it: | 1 | 2 | 3 | These can be added

to one at a time. A few minutes' practice daily at pointing at the numerals with a stick and naming them should help familiarise the class with these. Each child should be given his own individual number strip with a set of spare cards with the numerals on one side and the appropriate number of pips on the other. They can then practise arranging them in numerical order or matching the pips with the appropriate numeral.

Stepping stones can be drawn with chalk in the playground and numbered. They should be about a child's footstep apart and are stepped over and counted both forwards and backwards. Another game is to draw out three areas in the playground and print the numerals 1,2 and 3 on them. The children run round and, when a whistle is blown, must stop. You then call out a number and they must run to that area.

Table games

Introduce numerals one at a time on the programmed dice used for table games so that there is a combination of pips and numerals:

Materials

Margarine cartons, tins or boxes. A collection of counters or small objects such as acorns, beads, etc. Print the numerals on the sides of the boxes or tins. See who can fill their boxes first with the right number of objects.

HANG THEM ON THE HOOKS

Materials

A row of hooks screwed into a batten of wood and mounted on the wall. Stiff card with loops or rings to hang them by. Numerals are printed on the cards. A daily job for each pupil in turn is to hang the cards in the correct sequential order. When there are enough numerals the pupils can find their own birthday age or the day of the month as well.

JOINING THE DOTS

A quiet occupation and one that is usually enjoyed is that of joining dots in numbered order to make a picture. When children only recognise five or six numerals, this is not easy.

One suggestion is a star or pentagram. After practice in joining the dots the children may be able to draw this shape freehand and this can be used for Christmas decorations and cards:

The line between
1 and 5 should be
drawn by the
teacher.

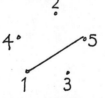

The order in which numerals are learnt is a personal matter. A pupil often recognises the number of his own age, especially when he receives birthday cards with it on. Make use of these and perhaps collect cards with numbers on. He may know a number which seems a difficult one because it is the number of his house or even his telephone number. Let pupils see if they can find their birthday number anywhere else when they go for a walk, for example, on garage doors, buses or house doors; or when they come indoors, on clocks, telephones, calendars, etc.

Cardboard cutouts of birthday numbers could be mounted on stiff card with glue. With a soft piece of paper laid over the top and a crayon or soft pencil, the child could make a 'rubbing' of his own number, rather like a brass rubbing. Instead of cardboard shapes you could buy some house door numbers from an ironmonger or DIY shop and use those. If you buy a few sets you can play a hiding game. Hide the numbers around the room (at first they should be visible, for example, on chairs or shelves or on the floor). The players should line up and when a number is said (five), they see who can find the numeral first. Duplicates of each number prevent excessive frustration, for then the slower ones can succeed in finding the right number. You could vary the game. Instead of saying a number you could hold up a playing card, for

example: The pupils again must search for a five after

counting the spots or guessing how many it is. Or you could scatter balls or conkers around the room. Each child is given a basket, and when a numeral is held up they have to gather that number of objects in their basket.

These are plastic house numbers which were bought at the local ironmongers. They can be stuck onto cards and have a raised edge which makes an excellent rubbing. They are called Silverthorne and cost only a few pence each.

To be able to count out ten objects accurately is an important milestone. Our number system is based on ten figures for the simple reason that we all have ten fingers. Each finger is known as a digit.

By now some of our children will have advanced well beyond ten in their rote counting, but we must not be surprised if they still make mistakes when asked to count out, for example, eight potatoes. Rose Griffiths, an experienced maths teacher, states that in an average group of five-year-olds less than half of them are likely to be able to count more than eight objects accurately and consistently. The greater the number of objects, the longer the concentration span and the greater the likelihood of co-ordination errors creeping in.

Children with learning difficulties will vary tremendously. Some will take many years before they can cope with more than a few numbers of objects, whilst a few may show surprising numerical ability.

It is important that we allow each child to travel at his own pace if we are aiming at the understanding of number.

The ALPS
Here we spell out the stages of learning to progress up the numerical mountain, always remembering to start at the bottom!

1   A   *Active experience.* Throughout this book we stress the importance of active involvement with real events and objects to build up number concepts, for example, playing with bricks, collecting, the rhythmic banging of a drum.

2   L   *Language.* In order to consolidate this active experience we need appropriate language to express new ideas and

to understand directions, for example, more, less, bigger, first, last.

3 P *Pictures* and patterns, in order to recall and record our experiences with real objects. Pictures can be used to represent objects, for example, pictures of three rabbits, or patterns can be used:

Patterns introduce the abstract quality of numbers.

4 S *Symbols*. Not until we are able to count real objects and talk about them and count pictures and patterns, are we ready to record and recognise the conventional symbols or numerals, for example:

$$3$$

Addition and subtraction of numbers under ten

HOW MANY MORE ARE THERE?

The rules of addition and subtraction do not have to be learnt separately as they are just two facets of the same fundamental process.

In order to understand this process it is important that children grasp the concept of MORE. When putting out the chairs or giving out the milk, they discover, by matching, that there are more chairs than children or more children than bottles of milk. It is important to make sure that they *do* have this concept before taking the next step, of beginning to count and compare the two quantities. For example, if there are six chairs and only four children, how many extra chairs are there? The answer, of course, is two. At first the children may need to work this out by matching and sitting on the chairs and seeing how many are left over. Later they will be able to tell you the difference between four and six without matching.

The same mathematical process can be expressed either as an addition sum: $6 = 4 + 2$, or as a subtraction sum: $6 - 4 = 2$. That is, six is the same as four and two more, or the difference between six and four is two.

One way of finding the difference between two quantities is by counting on, and this is something your pupils need to practise.

When it comes to larger numbers, counting on can be very laborious. Most adults do not need to count on with their fingers! They probably know without thinking the number bonds of six—that they can be one and five, two and four, three and three, and so on.

The activities in this chapter are designed to give children the idea of more and more than, practice in comparing two quantities and finding out how much bigger one is than the other, and familiarity with number bonds up to ten. This will give them a sound foundation for both addition and subtraction of numbers.

So far we have only mentioned two rules: addition and subtraction. What about the other two: multiplication and division?

Multiplication and division

Multiplication is really a quick way of doing addition with equal quantities, that is, we could add four and four and four and four and four rather laboriously, but if we have learnt our tables we can quickly find the answer: five fours are twenty. Similarly, division is a form of subtraction of equal quantities. Instead of taking four from twenty and then four from sixteen and then four from twelve and four from eight, we can quickly calculate the answer if we know that five fours are the same as twenty. A beginning will be made in counting in twos and threes at this stage.

GETTING THE IDEA OF MORE AND MORE THAN

Before introducing the idea of *one* more, the children must acquire a general understanding of the word *more*. This is gained through talking about active daily experiences. Before understanding 'more than' most children will have gained a general idea of the meaning of 'more' at meal times. 'Do you want some more potatoes?' or, 'Would you like some more milk?'

However, you still need to introduce the word in its comparative sense. Let the class get into two groups with the boys on one side and the girls on the other. 'Are there more boys than girls, or more girls than boys?' To answer these questions each boy could be told to find a partner from amongst the girls. Some boys may be left without partners and then you can point out that there are more boys than girls.

To continue this activity, each member of the class could take some bricks and the boys could build a tower with their bricks and then the girls build a tower alongside. They could then discuss with you the *difference* between the two towers. One has more bricks than the other and so on. This is a good introduction to subtraction which is now introduced in schools as the *difference* between two numbers rather than with the old idea of *taking away*.

Using squared paper, the pupils could draw the two piles of bricks and colour them in and find how many more bricks there were in one pile than in the other. You could also give them a little exercise by drawing the boys in one circle and the girls in another. They must link each girl with a boy by drawing a line and then see how many are without partners.

This activity could be turned into a graph to hang on the wall. Each boy could be given a blue square of sticky paper and each girl a pink square. A large sheet of sugar paper is laid out on the table with four vertical lines drawn on it. The boys stick their squares of paper one above each other in the left-hand column and the girls do the same in the right-hand column. Of course, they could also print their names on the squares. Encourage the children to count how many there are in each column and to see whether there are more boys or more girls in the class. When they can do this they could go on to find out how many more boys or girls there are. This graph can be put to further use when the register is taken. If a child is away the square could be temporarily covered over and the number of boys or girls recounted. The children can use this graph to check when they are giving out milk or saying how many will be staying to dinner.

ONE AND ONE MORE IS TWO . . .
Counting on is a practical way of checking the cost of items in shops and in getting change. The first step towards understanding addition or counting on is to add just one more at a time. This should be practised in many different situations so that it becomes second nature.

Steps
Count on as you slowly climb the steps—'One step, one and one more is two, two and one more is three, three and one more is four,' and so on.

Beads
Give out threading laces with one bead already threaded. Each child chooses the colour of the next bead and threads it. See if they can finish the sentence, 'One and one more makes . . .'

SHARING OUT TREATS
Children often bring treats to school for the mid-morning break. Make a little ritual of sharing these round. In the first round each pupil has one, in the second round they have one and one more and so on. As before, see if they can finish the sentence, 'Two and one more makes . . .' and so on.

A step diagram could also be displayed on the wall with numerals under each column. The teacher can then help the pupils to count the steps on the diagram as they counted the real steps, that is, 'One and one more makes two . . .'

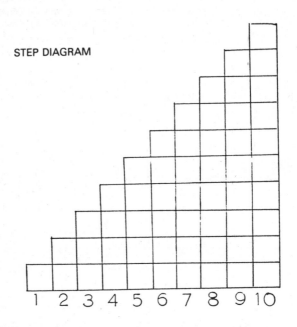

STEP DIAGRAM

1 2 3 4 5 6 7 8 9 10

NUMBER BONDS: PARTITIONING

The immediate recognition of number bonds is of great practical value. Most of us recognise the number bonds up to ten and use this knowledge daily to check out change. For example, if a purchase costs 27 pence we know immediately that we need 3p change from 30p. This instinctive knowledge can only develop through repeated practical experience.

If introduced to the idea of partitioning early on, a child will have a sure foundation for addition and subtraction. Starting with just three bricks and a piece of string, pupils can discover how many different ways they can separate them, as follows:

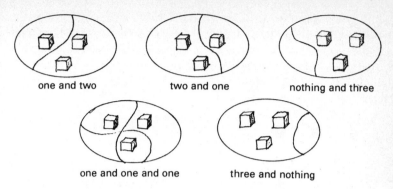

one and two   two and one   nothing and three

one and one and one   three and nothing

If pupils then describe what they have done to the parent or teacher—'Three is the same as two and one more' or 'One and two more', she will be able to check their understanding of number bonds. Remember, it is not always obvious to a child that one and two more is the same as two and one more.

Picture sums
Stories can be introduced at this point to provide extra experience alongside practical activities, and these can lead to *picture* sums.

Three blind mice
This could arise from singing the nursery rhyme. Model mice could be made with Playdoh, with string tails attached.

Everyone should have a chance to count the mice before the teacher pretends to be the farmer's wife and cuts off one tail (with scissors rather than a carving knife). 'How many mice now?' 'Three.' 'How many with tails?' 'Two.' 'How many without tails?'. 'One.' Then another tail gets cut off, and so on.

Pictures can then be drawn on the board or on a large sheet of paper for the children to retell the story sequence:

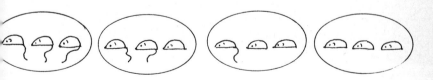

Other stories around the number three could also be told, for example, *Goldilocks and the Three Bears* or *Three Little Pigs.*

At this stage an introduction could be made to pictorial sums with a few conventional symbols, as follows:

The conventional symbols plus (+) and equals (=) have been included in the drawing. Do not introduce these to your pupils in isolation, but possibly point to them as you 'read' the story picture over and over again. 'Three is the same number as three (with tails) and no more'. 'Three is the same as two (with tails) and one more (without a tail). 'Three is the same as one (with a tail) and two more (without tails).'

You do not want to give the impression that three animals must always be of the same kind, and more picture sums with different animals can be drawn and read. Perhaps miniature animals could be involved and the rule made that no one is allowed more than three animals which can be either rabbits or cats. Each pupil chooses his three animals and arranges them in a row. These can then be the basis for more picture sums:

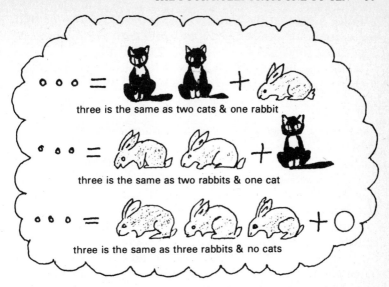

three is the same as two cats & one rabbit

three is the same as two rabbits & one cat

three is the same as three rabbits & no cats

When the number bonds of three have been well consolidated, higher numbers can be introduced. The ALPS sequence should be followed for each new number. The *activity* is probably best centred around the children themselves. Perhaps a group of four children could come out with different-coloured shoes. They could stand together to be counted and then all with brown shoes move to the left. Those with brown shoes are then counted and then those without brown shoes, demonstrating the sum, 'Four is the same as three with brown shoes and one without brown shoes' and so on.

The group of four could then reform and a new attribute be chosen: perhaps those with glasses could move to the left—'four is the same as two with glasses and two without glasses'—or the colour of their hair could be chosen, or those dressed in blue, or the boys and the girls.

Hands can be used for the number FIVE
Everyone holds up one hand and counts the
number of fingers with the other hand. Then
one finger is hidden which gives 'Five is the
same as four fingers up and one down,' and so
on.

*More activities with farm animals, and lengths
of string or dowelling*
Each child is given a number of farm animals and lengths of
string or dowelling with which to make fences. No child should
have more than two kinds of animal at this stage, nor should he
have more animals than he can count out accurately. His task is
to divide the animals into two fields when he has counted them.
He can then tell you a story about his animals, for example,
why some are in one field and some in another (perhaps all the
fierce animals have been put together in one field). Let them
then tell you the number story—eight animals is the same as
five fierce animals and three tame animals.

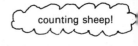

counting sheep!

They could then arrange the animals differently with,
perhaps, the big animals in one field and the small ones in
another.
Many different materials can be used, such as bricks
or beads. Only when the pupils are competent orally should
they attempt to record their stories as was done with the
mice.

Active games
Whatever number bonds the pupils are working on at the
moment can be practised in movement sessions in the hall or
playground.
A group of pupils is first counted and then told they can

choose which side of the room to run to. Each group is counted and it is found that the eight pupils are now in two groups: five in one group and three in the other. The teacher then names one or two pupils to change ends so that the grouping changes and is again counted. When they know the game, a pupil could change roles with the teacher.

Skittles
The pupils in the class could decide how many skittles to use and check them over. After each player has had a turn he could count how many skittles are down (his score) and then how many are still standing, and perhaps comment, 'Three down and three still standing are the same as six'. In this activity the game is the most important thing and can be played with different numbers of skittles, which will give practice in number bonds especially if the pupils get into the habit of counting how many are down and how many are left standing after each turn. Perhaps the pupils will want later to record

their scores in *picture* form, either on a duplicated sheet or on the blackboard.

After their shot they could draw how many skittles they had managed to get down in the first box and then the number left standing in the second and the total number of skittles in the third.

This record can also be a talking point: 'Ann had three skittles down and three left standing and that is the same as six skittles altogether.' Discussion might arise as to who had the highest score, and so on.

SCORE SHEET

Subtraction

Children who have become familiar with number bonds and addition should be ready for games involving taking away. Start with small numbers at first.

THE ROBBER STORY

Materials: bean bags.

A small number of bean bags are arranged on the floor with the children sitting round them. These are bags of gold and must be carefully counted because there may be a robber about who comes in the night to steal the treasure. When everybody knows how many bags of gold they have to guard they close their eyes and fall asleep. The robber will not come as long as anyone is peeping. Quietly the robber (teacher) steals a bag of gold and wakens the sleepers. 'Has anything gone? How many bags are there?' See if anyone can tell and accept their answer no matter how they arrived at it. For example, four and one is the same as five, four is one less than five, the difference between four and five is one.

This game can be played many times and pupils can take turns to be the robber.

Later, individual 'robber' puzzles can be duplicated and handed round for them to work on at their desks.

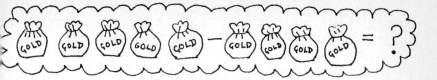

The pupils can then talk about their picture sums: for example, the difference between five and four is one, or five is one more than four—so one must have gone.

Puzzles with playing cards
Two playing cards are placed face up on the table. Start with low denomination cards, perhaps a two and a three. The pupil counts the pips on the two cards—five. The pupil shuts his eyes and the teacher turns a card over. The game is to guess the number of pips on this card. Pairs of pupils can then play this game together and later be given picture puzzles to work out.

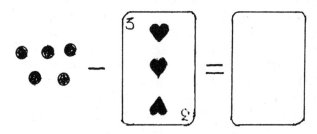

DAILY PRACTICE
The practice provided by daily events is most important in consolidating the understanding of numerical relationships. If parents, teachers and teaching aides are aware of individual levels of ability, they can all seize opportunities which occur naturally in the course of the day.

Meal times provide many opportunities and, if a child has a helping of prunes, for instance, it does not take a minute to suggest that he counts them and, when some have been eaten, counts how many are left and tells you how many he has eaten. He can tell you a little story: 'I had six cherries and ate two and four were left.'

The daily register makes another opportunity so long as the

child is up to dealing with the number in the class. For example, if there are nine pupils in the class and two are away, perhaps one of the pupils could tell how many are left so that you know how many bottles of milk to bring up or how many dinners to order. For beginners it is often easiest to count how many children are there and then work out how many are absent by counting on from the larger number.

Practice in multiplication and division

A start can be made with the idea of multiplication or equal addition with numbers up to ten.

This is again best introduced in a practical activity. Perhaps the boys' wellingtons could be collected up in a heap and the pupils could help to sort them out in pairs and count them. When they have counted them you could point out that there are four pairs for four boys, so four pairs make eight boots. Another time they could be shown a quick way of counting in twos—'two, four, six, eight.' When this has been practised with boots, shoes, dancing pumps and gloves, perhaps you could count out in a new way—one two is two, two twos are four, three twos are six, four twos are eight and five twos are ten.

Vary your questions about the boots: sometimes give them a row of boots and, when they have counted them, see if they can tell you how many pairs six boots will be, for instance.

If you wish you can prepare *work cards* as well, with pictures of pairs of footwear, gloves, or faces in which to count the eyes.

Owl work card. How many eyes?

Make completing the work cards into a race, to dissuade your pupils from counting the eyes, shoes, etc., singly. They should either count in twos—two, four, six, eight—or say four twos are eight.

Other ways can be devised to encourage counting in twos or remembering the table. Why not ask a few pupils to stand in a line and turn their backs on the class. The race is to see who is the first to say how many eyes they have between them. Alternatively, a group of pupils could sit with their feet hidden behind a screen and the class could guess how many shoes there were.

Division with rabbits

Cut out a set of cardboard rabbits and hide them behind a screen so that only their ears are visible. See who can tell you how many rabbits are sitting behind the screen. Pupils can check their answer by taking the screen away and counting.

How many rabbits are hidden behind this wall?

A show of hands

Let a group of pupils hide behind a screen and raise their hands.

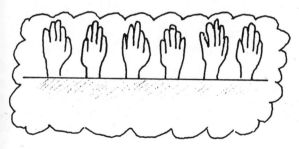

How many children are hidden behind this screen?

Parents in particular will be able to give their children practical problems of this kind when sorting out the socks from the laundry, or the knitting needles, perhaps.

Naturally these and similar puzzles can also be made into pictorial work cards. These have their place, but the practical ability to solve real problems should take priority.

Fishes' eyes

Magnetic fishing games can be bought commercially and adapted as number games for different stages. Or what about a little DIY?

Materials for making a magnetic fishing game
The rods: lengths of bamboo or dowelling, lengths of string for
    the lines, small magnets to tie onto the lines.
The fish: white cardboard, paper fasteners, paints.
The pond: a cardboard box big enough to spread a shoal of fish
    out on the bottom so that they are not on top of one another.

To make the fish
Cut out a fish-shaped template and use it to make three cardboard fish shapes for each fish. Paint eyes, fins and so on, on two of the three shapes and slip a paper fastener over the nose of the third fish shape.

Glue these three shapes firmly together, with the paper fastener in the middle of the sandwich as shown. It is well worth taking some trouble over making these fish because if covered with library film they can be 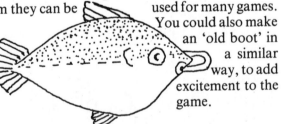 used for many games. You could also make an 'old boot' in a similar way, to add excitement to the game.

To play
Each player dangles his or her rod over the box in which the fish and the boots have been placed. They draw them up to see whether they have caught a fish or a boot or nothing. At the end, each player counts his fish (boots score nothing) and the

final score is the number of eyes. Encourage the players to calculate these by saying three twos, etc., or by counting in twos.

ADDITION FISH

For practice in addition, a pull-off label can be affixed to each fish, using 'post-it' cover-up tape. Numbers of spots can be printed on the labels. At the end of the game each player calculates his or her total score by 'counting on'. Once the pupils are familiar with numerals, these can be printed on the fish instead of the spots.

Ten is a very special number in our counting system and in our decimal coinage. To be able to count out coins or objects into piles of ten without mistakes, and to remember that 9 and 1, 8 and 2, 7 and 3, etc., all make ten, is a sure foundation for calculations and money handling. Without this foundation there can be no understanding of the fact that fourteen is ten and four more, that forty is four tens or that 327 is three hundreds and two tens and seven units.

Our knowledge of the numbers that add up to ten is essential for checking change when shopping.

Be sure that this foundation is laid before attempting to go on to the later sections of this book. The fact that some of our pupils can count up to twenty or sixty is no guarantee that they have reached this understanding. Try out the activities in this chapter and make sure. Starting with activities to consolidate knowledge of the number ten, pictures and symbols will be introduced at the end of this chapter.

COUNTING OUT IN TENS

Materials
Lollipop sticks and elastic bands, beads and laces, bricks or unifix bricks, finger paints and paper, lots of one penny pieces. These are only a beginning. Remember that the greater the variety of materials used the better.

1   Give each pupil a pile of lollipop sticks and elastic bands. As them to see how many bundles of ten sticks they can make before you come round again to check. Do not forget to talk about what you are doing: let each pupil tell you how many bundles he has made and how many sticks are in each bundle. Comment on who has made the most bundles or who was the quickest, mention the fact if one of the bundles is too small or too large and will have to be counted again, and so on.

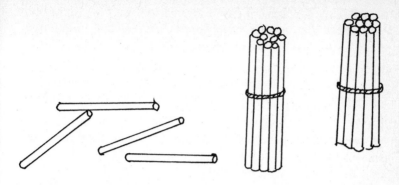

2 Each pupil has a tub full of wooden beads and several laces to string them on. See how quickly they can string them on the laces with just ten beads on each lace. Again the discussion of results is important as it introduces the language of numeracy and is also a check on each pupil's understanding.

'Are they both the same length?'

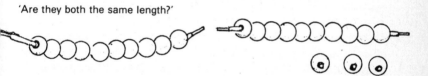

3 Each pupil has a pile of bricks and the task is to see how many towers of ten bricks they can make in two minutes. Note which pupils realise they do not have to count the bricks each time.

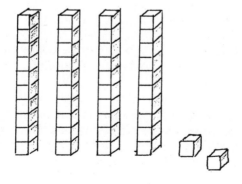

4   All the class make their hand prints with finger paint on a large sheet of paper. They first count their own fingers and then draw a ring around each group of ten fingers on the chart.

5   Each pupil has a box of 1p coins and counts them out into piles of ten. They discuss how many piles they have managed to make and how many coins are left over, and which pupil has made the most piles.

Look out for other opportunities for counting out in tens and meanwhile record which pupils:
>   made mistakes,
>   needed your help,
>   were unable to say how many piles they had made,
>   counted out each pile separately,
>   were very slow.
Which ones:
>   made no mistakes,
>   did not need help,
>   were able to tell you how many piles they had,
>   did not need to count each pile separately,
>   could sort out in tens quickly and accurately.
The first group probably need more practice. The second group should be ready to go on to the next section.

NUMBER BONDS OF TEN
Through daily experience most of us can immediately recall the numbers which add up to ten. When we have spent seven pence we know at once that we need three pence change. When adding up a column of figures we instinctively group them together in tens. We know that five twos are the same as ten without having to think about it, and so on.

Without this knowledge dealing with figures would be very difficult, slow and tedious. Extra practice with these number bonds will be needed by some of our pupils.

Finger games
Hold up both hands and make sure that everyone has counted the number of fingers to be seen. Hide one finger behind your hand and ask, 'How many fingers can you see now?' The answer will be nine. Allow counting of the fingers if this is

needed, but encourage a quick answer. Reveal the finger to show that it is still there and explain how nine fingers on view and one hidden are the same as ten fingers. 'Nine and one more is the same as ten. Ten is nine and one more. Nine is one less than ten. Ten, take away one, is nine'. Play this game again and hide a different number of fingers each time. See whether the pupils know how to describe it when all the fingers are hidden—nothing and ten more is the same as ten.

Let the pupils play the game together in pairs. Give them a pair of gloves so that they can practise bending down the fingers and recording the sum in drawing.

NAIL VARNISH

This game should appeal to the girls, and perhaps to some boys also. Provide a few bottles of nail varnish of different colours. Instruct the pupils to choose a colour and to varnish one nail at a time, and then give it time to dry before varnishing another. While the varnish is drying they should count their nails, for example, one varnished and nine plain is the same as ten. They can then continue to varnish another nail in the same way.

Let them now work in pairs and, given a large sheet of paper and crayons, draw around each other's hands until they have drawn ten pairs of hands underneath one another. They then colour one pair of nails and then two, and so on. This can be displayed on the wall, making sure that each pupil can describe what has happened verbally. 'One varnished and nine plain is the same as ten,' and so on.

Use this chart for practice in mental arithmetic, for example: 'Three and how many more are the same as ten?' 'Ten take away seven is the same as ＿ ＿ ＿ ＿?'

Handling money

It is important to become familiar with handling ten one pence pieces before being expected to handle larger sums. Whenever possible real money and real purchases should be made. It is a good idea to give pupils a standard amount of pocket money to spend (ten pence at a time) so that they can get used to what that will buy. A school tuck shop with low prices makes a good beginning. One school instigated a 'health food' tuck shop where students could buy a carrot or an apple, etc., for a few pence. The hand chart can be used to help work out what one is able to buy. Similarly, shopping at real shops will be arranged by parents and teachers. However, practice and games in the classroom will help to consolidate the practical experience outside.

Money games
These games involve more rules than the activities already described, for instance 'reading' a face of a dice or a playing card and translating this into a number of coins to be placed, taking turns and continuing the game without adult direction. It is often important for the teacher to join in the game initially to ensure that every player knows the rules and can apply them. Then small groups can play together, starting with two people and gradually increasing the size of the group. As these are games of chance, children with mixed ability can enjoy playing together. For a child with a short attention span it is best to have a small group, as waiting one's turn may be difficult for them. Once the games have been learnt they can be played at home with parents, siblings or friends.

FILL A TRAY

Apparatus
A pile of 1p and 10p coins (cardboard or plastic coins *can* be used, but it is much better to get the children used to handling real money).
Trays: Mark out ten circles onto a stout piece of card (2.5 cm (1 in) diameter). Make one card for each player. Better still, collect sauce or vinegar bottle tops from parents, friends and colleagues and glue ten of these onto each card or tray.
Dice: Start by using programmed dice. These are made from wooden cubes with gummed paper spots stuck onto the faces. Two faces have one spot only, one face has two spots, one three, one four and one has no spots. Alternatives to dice are a spinner similarly marked, or a pile of playing cards (denominations one to five only).

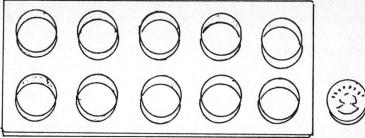

To play
The coins are placed in a container in the middle of the table.
Each player has a ten-place tray and he shakes the dice or turns
over a playing card and places the right number of one penny
coins in the circles on the tray. If a player throws a blank on the
dice he misses a turn. The player who fills his tray first is the
winner but he must throw the exact number to finish. He then
exchanges his coins for a ten pence piece. If the players are still
keen they can continue the game and try for another ten pence.
This game helps to reinforce the number bonds of ten.

Number towers
This game is a popular alternative to the ten pennies game.

Apparatus
Each player needs a simple ring stack just tall enough to stack
ten rings. Programmed dice, spinners or playing cards are used
as in the previous game.

Materials
Lengths of dowelling, plywood or board 10 mm thick, tenon
saw, drill and bit slightly larger than the dowelling, carpenter's
glue.

To make
Cut 110 mm lengths of dowelling (one for each player). Cut
pieces of wood for stands (70 mm square) and drill a hole in the
centre to fit the dowel. Glue the length of dowel into the hole so
that 100 mm are free standing.

Cut out ten squares of plywood (30 mm × 30 mm) for each player. Drill a hole in the centre of each slightly larger in diameter than the dowelling. These are then sanded and dyed so that each player has a different coloured set of rings.

To play
The rings are placed in the centre of the table and each player chooses a colour. Either a dice is thrown by a player or a card is turned up or a spinner is used. The player threads the number of rings shown onto his stack. The first player to fill his stack is the winner but the last throw must be the exact number to finish the stack; if it is too many the player misses a turn.

The game can be made more difficult if each player has to fill two stacks to win. When one stack is filled the rings are removed and placed in a bag marked 10, and then the player proceeds to fill a second bag.

Using playing cards
Packs of cards with the picture cards and jokers removed can be used for a variety of games that give practice in number bonds. Here are a few.

FIND THE TENS
A game for one to four players round the table.

To play
The cards are spread out face up on the table. The teacher models the procedure by selecting two cards which together add up to ten and the players count the pips on the cards to check that she is right. Each player in turn selects two cards which together add up to ten and (if they are correct) keeps the cards. The game continues until no more tens can be made. The players then count how many pairs of cards they have collected and discuss who has the most or has won.

RACING TENS
The cards are spread out as before and the teacher holds up a card and the players have to find another card which will make the pair add up to ten. The player who finds one first keeps the pair.

HIDDEN TENS
This time the cards are distributed, face up, round the room on chairs and tables. The teacher, with a spare pack, holds up a card and the players have to search round the room for its complementary pair.

PAIRS OR PELMANISM FOR BONDS OF TEN
The players need to be familiar with the easier version of the game where two identical cards have to be turned up before attempting this harder game.

To play
The cards are placed face down on the table. Two suits of cards are enough to start with (nine pairs). Players take turns to turn over any two cards on the table. If the two cards add up to ten, the player keeps them. If not they are turned back again without altering their position on the table. The players are encouraged to watch one another so that they can remember the position of the cards on the table. The winner is the player who collects the most pairs. At they finish, each player counts how many pairs he has collected and discussion is encouraged.

INTRODUCING NUMERALS
Variations of the above games can now be made to increase the pupil's skill in recognising the numerals 1,2,3,4,5,6,7,8,9. Dice can be made with numerals on the faces instead of spots, or spinners with numerals can be used. Simple games can be played and the scores written up on a board, for example Tiddlywinks or Tiddly Target.

Tiddly Target
The pot is placed in the centre of the play area and two concentric rings are drawn around it: the first four inches and the second eight inches in diameter. The players arrange their winks at an agreed distance from the pot and squidge them in turn, scoring three points for any that land in the pot, two for those in the inner circle and one for those in the outer circle. Once a wink has landed in a circle it cannot be squidged again. When all the winks have been played the scores are added up.

Darts

Safety darts can be bought at most toy shops and Early Learning Centres. The segments are usually numbered one to ten, ten being the bull's eye. There are many versions of this game and it is best to start with a version which is simple and does not last too long.

UP TO TEN

This is played like 'Round the Clock'. The players have to hit the numbers one to ten consecutively in order to score, and the first player to reach number ten is the winner. This helps the players to become familiar with 'reading' the numerals and with recognising the order of sequence.

ONE THROW TURNS

In this game each player throws only one dart per turn and the aim is to win the highest score. Do not forget to encourage discussion of who has scored the most, for example, 'Rachel has scored nine and Peter has scored seven. Has Rachel more or less than Peter? How many more?'

Pelmanism or Pairs with numerals

Packs of blank playing cards can be ordered from Waddingtons and are useful for a variety of games. Using Letraset or a stencil, print the numerals 1,2,3,4,5,6,7,8,9 on the faces of four sets of cards, that is, 36 cards. Start by using only half of the pack—18 cards or 9 pairs. For recognition of numerals play the game in the conventional way—two identical cards have to be turned up and 'read' to form a pair. Later the version of the game with bonds of ten can be played.

More formal work

With the introduction of numerals we have reached the symbolic stage of our ALPS sequence and are ready to start on more formal individual work. This will be especially important for pupils who are to be integrated into a mainstream class or who are already attending an infant or junior school in the mainstream, or for older pupils who are starting further education courses in literacy and numeracy. However, remember that some of your pupils may not be ready for this but may need more practical consolidation.

Before going on to table-top work of a more formal kind, make sure that each pupil can do the following:

1   recognise and name the numeral cards quickly,
2   match numeral cards with the correct playing card,
3   find two playing cards which together add up to ten without prompting,
4   find two numeral cards which together add up to ten without prompting.

Writing down 'sums' is just a way of recording what you can already do in your head, and a pupil who cannot recognise his number bonds is not really ready to record them.

Materials
Half a pack of playing cards for each pupil or pair of pupils, without the picture cards. One set of printed numeral cards for each pupil, that is, 1,2,3,4,5,6,7,8,9,10, together with one plus (+) and one equals (=) card. Duplicated sum sheets, pencils and erasers.

PROCEDURE

Warm up
Pupils lay out their numeral cards in order and match them with a row of playing cards.

The parent or teacher demonstrates laying out a row of cards as a sum, putting the 'ten' card down first on the right and then helping the pupils to choose two cards which add up to ten.

Pupils and teacher should then read this sum: 'Six and four more is the same number as ten.'

Pupils are then invited to make more rows of numbers to add up to ten. Give them the opportunity to do as many as they can on their own. Choose one of these pattern sums and let them place the correct numeral cards under the playing cards. Insert the plus and equals cards in the right places and show them that + stands for 'and . . . more' and = stands for 'is the same'.

This sum can then be copied on prepared worksheets, and so on.

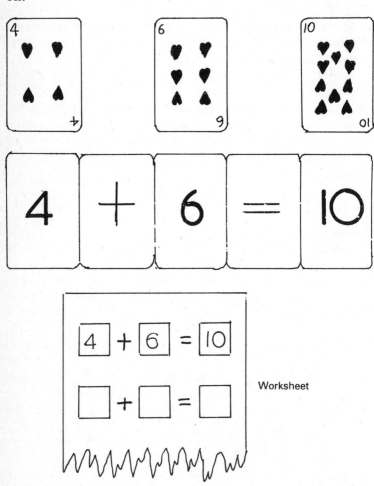

Worksheet

Subtraction

A pupil who knows his number bonds and can count on with numbers under ten should have no difficulty with subtraction which is just the other side of the coin of addition. For instance, if we know that ten is the same number as seven and three, it is a small step to realise that if someone takes three away from ten, then seven will be left, or, to put it another way, seven is three less than ten.

Everyday life provides many examples of simple addition and subtraction and pupils should be encouraged to express these in words.

At meal times they could count the number of prunes on their plate and, when some have been eaten, count how many are left. They should be able to express this in a story: 'I had six prunes and ate two and had four left.' The daily register gives practice in subtraction with a purpose, for example: 'There are nine pupils in the class and two are absent. How many are present so that we can order the right number of bottles of milk or lunches?' Or the problem to be solved by the class can be expressed another way: 'There are seven pupils present and there should be nine. How many are away?'

Shopping, either outside or at the school tuckshop, gives more practice with a purpose. If pupils are given a regular ten pence as 'spends' they can count their change: 'I have two pence left, how much have I spent? I must have spent eight pence.' Some pupils will know the answer immediately and the others should be encouraged to 'count on' (complementary addition), which is how change is very often calculated in shops.

PUZZLES

The card games described above can be varied to include subtraction as well as addition. Two cards can be laid face up on the table and the pupils encouraged to guess the total number of pips and then to check by counting. They then shut their eyes and one card is turned over. The pupils guess the number on this card and also see how many are left and 'count on' to see if they are right. Eventually they turn the card over to make sure.

Pupils can then work in pairs with these puzzles. The minus

sign need not be introduced at this stage, but worksheets on which you have to find the missing number can be made, and also the same puzzles can be played with numeral cards rather than playing cards.

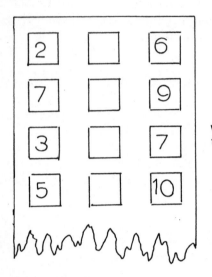

WORKSHEET
find the missing number

Multiplication and division

We saw how addition and subtraction could be thought of as two sides of the same coin, both of which depended on an ability to count on and to recognise number bonds. Similarly with multiplication and division. Multiplication is just a quick way of calculating sums with repeated equal addition. For example, instead of adding $8 + 8 + 8 + 8 + 8 + 8$ we can take a short cut and count the number of eights (six), and come up with the answer: 48. Similarly, we could share our 48 out laboriously between eight boxes and find we could put six in each or take a short cut and ask how many eights in forty-eight. Our ability to take the short cut depends on our knowledge of multiplication tables. When dealing with numbers under ten these need not yet be considered.

In the next section, on counting, the groundwork of multiplication and division will be laid down.

Section Three

MORE THAN TEN

Pupils who are well able to count up to twenty or beyond can
now begin a new kind of rhythmic counting.
    The counting rhyme 'Two, four, six, eight
                              Mary at the cottage gate.'
makes a good introduction to counting in twos, for instance.
Many things come in pairs, pairs of shoes, pairs of socks, two
eyes, two arms, two legs and two ears.
    Encourage pupils to count the lines of wellies, slippers or
shoes, first normally and then by whispering the odd numbers
and stressing the even numbers: one,*two*,three *four*,five,*six*,
seven,*eight*, and so on.
    See if anyone can manage to say the odd numbers under their
breath silently and count out loud in twos: . . . .,two,. . . .,
four,. . . .,six,. . . .,eight. Gradually the odd numbers can be
left out for rhythmical counting in twos. Think of all the ways
this can be practised. Pairs of socks or gloves can be pegged
onto a line and counted in twos. Pupils could line up in a row
so that their shoes can be counted, or their legs or arms or ears.
When this counting in twos is fairly slick you can introduce
variations: for instance, when counting a line of wellies you
could remove them one pair at a time and count backwards in
twos: eight,six,four,two. Stepping stones in the playground
give further practice.

Games to play
A waste-paper bin is placed in the middle of the floor and the
players stand in a circle round it. Each player is given the same
number of bean bags and they take turns throwing them into
the bin. Each goal counts two points. If each player has
different-coloured bean bags, this makes for easy scoring at the
end, counting the score in twos.
    Later versions of this game could include counting in fives or

threes, etc. Rose Griffiths has described a good version of this game called 'Bean bag clowns' in her book *Maths through Play* (Macdonald).

NUMBER STRIPS
From now on number strips can be used by the pupils in many different ways and it is useful to duplicate a stock of these with numbers in rows of ten from one to twenty.

Each pupil is given one of these and chooses a colour with which to colour in all the even numbers.

1	2	3	4	5	6	7	8	9	10
11	12	13	14	15	16	17	18	19	20

One two is two, two twos are four
Do not be in too great a hurry to introduce the two-times table in this form. It *can* cause confusion if introduced too soon. How can *one* thing be *two* or *two* things *four*? The idea is a little less confusing in a practical setting, for example one *pair* of shoes is two shoes, two *pairs* are four, three *pairs* are six. When the pupils are ready the word 'twos' can be substituted for 'pairs'.

Division
The groundwork for division should be laid at the same time as multiplication. For instance, if we have ten unsorted shoes, how many pairs of shoes will that be? That is to say that ten divided into pairs is five. The reverse should also be introduced —that ten divided between five people will be two each.

Pupils can use their number strips to help them with these puzzles.

Pupils can be given a number of stick-on spots for 'eyes'. If I give you twelve, how many faces can you make? Encourage intelligent guessing, which can be checked as the faces are completed.

Counting in fives

With our decimal currency, counting in fives is more important than counting in threes or fours, and should be introduced first. Fingers on hands and gloves and numbers of toes on a foot make a good introduction.

Activities and language, including rhythmic counting, should precede pictorial work and use of symbols.

Bunches of five

Pupils sit round the table and in turn place a clenched fist on the table while all count, five, ten, fifteen fingers. At the end the hands are opened and the fingers counted singly. Gloves can be used to count out and then to record in picture form. Handprints on the wall can be used for checking that one glove is five fingers, two gloves are ten. With numerals added it can make a permanent 'table' for reference. A number strip can be coloured in fives by the pupils to keep for themselves.

Glove table

1	2	3	4	5	6	7	8	9	10
11	12	13	14	15	16	17	18	9	20

Number strip

Let pupils practise changing single pennies into five pence coins also.

Standing on four legs

Start with active observation to make the pupils aware of the objects round about which have four legs: tables, chairs, cats, dogs and cows. Play a form of 'I spy': 'I spy with my little eye something that has four legs.' This game is useful on a car journey, to see how many things with four legs can be seen out of the window.

Models can be used, and each pupil in turn has to choose something with four legs from a table-top array.

Patterns can then be used and a similar game played with pictures of shapes laid out on the table: squares, rectangles, diamonds, circles. The pupils have to select those with four *sides* this time.

After this the pupils will be ready to count the chair legs in a row, in fours. A wall chart can be put on the board to introduce the beginning of the four times table—one table has four legs, two tables have eight legs, and so on.

Wall chart

Counting in threes

See how many leaves with three lobes you can find on a walk, for example clover leaves. Play the pattern game that you played with the number four, but this time find the shapes with three sides, that is, the triangles.

Prepare a wall display with clover leaves to introduce the three times table. One leaf has three lobes, two leaves have six lobes and three leaves have nine lobes.

Pupils should be given new number strips to colour in threes and fours.

Wall chart for threes

Sharing
The idea of fair or equal shares is important to children at quite an early age. Make sure that everyone has plenty of opportunity to share things out in the course of the day—sweets, pencils, erasers, sheets of paper and so on. To begin with make sure that they have enough to go round without remainders, and let them find their own way of sharing out fairly so that everyone gets the same number. Do not forget the discussion which follows, 'I had ten sweets to share between five people and they each got two'. Do not be in a hurry to record such division sums and never use numbers too big for easy counting.

Up to now we have followed the ALPS plan to give children many opportunities, through action, language and pictures, to memorise many useful facts concerning numbers up to ten. They have become familiar with many different number bonds or families, for example that five and one more is the same as six, or that five is one less than six. Not until the pupils have been able to memorise such number bonds in practical situations or with the aid of pictures or patterns have we introduced the *symbols* which are used to record such knowledge. For instance, the number bonds of six can be recorded symbolically as $4 + 2 = 6$ and $1 + 5 = 6$. Number bonds have also been linked with subtraction of numbers under ten. Subtraction has been thought of as complementary addition, for example six is four and two more. Equal addition has also been introduced with small numbers (multiplication) and linked with equal subtraction or division. Pupils will now be familiar with counting out many more than ten objects and with counting in twos, threes, fours, and fives, and will have started to record their calculations also.

It is now important to introduce the idea of place values which forms the basis of our mathematical system and decimal system of coinage.

PLACE VALUES
Our system of mathematics is based on the number ten and we only need to use nine numerals and a nought to be able to record any conceivable number. The value of a numeral depends upon its place in the row, and reading from left to right the numeral '1' can stand for one hundred, one ten or one unit. The introduction of this simple device has revolutionised our ability to calculate, as you will realise if you try to add up a string of Roman numerals, for example V,IV,XI,CIX and VIII.

A start towards the understanding of place values through activity, language pictures and symbols will be made with numbers under twenty. Here are a few suggestions:

1   Empty the shelves of books and let the pupil make a pile of ten books for easy counting. Hand him another book and let him count on, 'ten, eleven.' Continue in this way, adding one more book at a time, until there are nineteen books or ten and nine more. Talk about it with your pupil, for example, 'Ten and one more is . . .?' or 'One pile and one more is . . .?' Let him shut his eyes while you arrange the books and see if he can tell you how many ten and six more is, for instance. Help him to realise how easy it is to guess how many ten and nine, eight, seven, six and five make. Just count the extra books, for example eight, and say, 'Eight-ten,' or 'eighteen', and so on.

2   BAGGING TENS

Materials
Small objects, beans, counters, beads or buttons. Bags with plastic ties or small boxes, such as matchboxes.
Procedure
Pupils are given piles of small objects (fewer than twenty). They are asked to sort them out and count out ten objects to be put in a bag and then place the spare objects beside the bag on the right-hand side. By counting on from ten the pupils discover how many beans there are, for instance.

One bag and three beans is thirteen beans

3   BUNDLES OF TEN

Materials
Cocktail sticks, straws, or pencils and rubber bands.
Procedure
These sticks should be counted as before and made into

bundles of ten fastened with a rubber band. The spare sticks should be placed on the right of the bundles. As before, pupils count on from ten and find that one bundle and four more is fourteen, and so on.

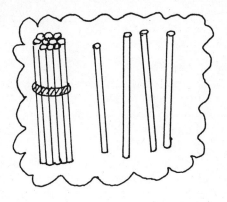

Picture sums

Materials
Duplicated sheets of pictures as shown below.

		13

The pupil's task is to record the number of bundles and then the number of loose sticks in the right-hand column. The first line has been completed. When the worksheet has been completed the totals should be read back to the teacher or parent, for example one bundle (ten) and three more is thirteen. Hopefully one bright spark may twig the easy way to arrive at the answer by reading the last numeral first e.g. six and then adding on the ten or 'teen' to get sixteen. If no one spots this, then the teacher will need to point it out. At this point the idea can be introduced that one bundle and no more is just ten and is written 10.

Using money
Make sure your pupils can sort out ten pence coins and one pence coins and name them. Do they know that one ten pence coin is equivalent to ten one pence coins? If not, try the game on p. 72 to consolidate this idea. Use ten pence and one pence coins for further practice in teens. Use real coins in a series of guessing games. Place a ten pence coin and some one pence coins on the table (make sure the one pence coins are on the right side of the ten pence coin from the pupils' point of view). See who can guess the total value first. Worksheets can then be made with paper coins or coin prints. (Philip and Tacey).

More formal work
Remember that being able to deal with numbers in a practical or pictorial way must precede the formal ability to record sums using numerals. When your pupils are fully competent in the activities described above it is time to move on to more formal work. First check that they are able to recognise the numbers 10,11,12,13,14,15,16,17,18 and 19, and also to print them. To test this, make a set of flash cards and give frequent quick bursts of practice with these in random order. Also reverse the process and dictate the numbers to them in random order for them to write down.

Until they can do this quickly and accurately it is too early to introduce more formal work. They may manage to get sums right with a struggle, but will fail to understand what they are doing.

Some of the class may be ready for more formal work with the numbers one to nineteen. For those who still need concrete help an abacus can be provided or bundles of sticks used as before, or unifix cubes can be used. Start with easy problems of addition, for example $10 + 3 = ?$ or $10 + 7 = ?$ (ten and three more is the same as . . . ?).

Then let them do the same calculations in reverse, for example $15 = 10 + ?$ (fifteen is the same as ten and how many more?).

SUBTRACTION
Practical work with bundles and sticks or unifix cubes should precede written work. The teacher places a bundle and a number of loose sticks on the table and the pupils say how many she has put down, for example sixteen. They then shut their eyes and either the bundle or the loose sticks are removed and the pupils say how many are left. They should now be ready to record these subtraction sums in their books, for example $15 - 5 = ?$, or $15 - 10 = ?$

Harder sums
Threading beads of two colours, unifix cubes, bundles of sticks or a simple abacus should be available. (Escor and Adams make a simple abacus which is available in good toy shops).

None of the sums should total more than nineteen at this stage, for example $7 + 5 = ?$

If they are using the beads as an aid, pupils could be given ten red beads only and then more beads of another colour. They should start using the red beads and only use another colour when these run out so that they can see that they have threaded ten red beads and added three more beads to make thirteen.

Similarly, they can calculate a subtraction such as $15 - 6 = ?$ using the threading beads. Again the red beads should be used up before another colour is used to make the fifteen beads. When this has been done the six beads are removed, leaving nine red beads as the answer.

Number bonds
Pupils should now be given the opportunity to experiment for themselves, using the beads as before or the abacus, so cementing the number bonds up to nineteen.

Starting with the red beads, the pupil chooses how many to thread on the lace. He then moves the beads along the string and records as many sums as possible, for example $14 + 1 = 15$, $13 + 2 = 15$, and so on. When all the possible sums have been recorded for that number of beads, the pupil can add more beads to the string and record another lot of sums.

An abacus can be used in a similar manner, or a line of coloured bricks. As the pupils become familiar with these number bonds they will only need the apparatus for checking. Subtraction sums can also be devised by the pupils themselves.

With practical demonstrations with piles of bricks, bundles of sticks, unifix bricks and the use of an abacus, the jump to counting in tens should not be too difficult and the numerical notation of 10,20,30,40,50,60,70,80,90 and even 100 can be introduced. For example, ten is written as one bundle and nothing more or 10, two bundles and nothing more are written as 20 . . . and ten bundles and nothing more are written as 100.

Extra practice in counting in tens can be gained by using the stepping stones, and these can also be counted backwards: 90,80,70,60 . . . Six bundles of sticks are six tens, and if this is said quickly it becomes sixty. Twenty and thirty are not so easy to guess but are nearly 'twoty' and 'threety!'

Worksheets can be prepared to practise notation:

🎋🎋	2	0
🎋🎋🎋🎋		
🎋🎋🎋🎋🎋		
🎋🎋		
🎋🎋🎋🎋🎋🎋🎋		
🎋🎋🎋🎋🎋🎋		
🎋		

The pupils record the number of bundles in the right hand column and then the number of loose sticks (none or 0) and then read out their answer: for example, two bundles and no more is twenty, or two tens and no more is twenty.

The ten times table
Having counted in tens and been able to fill up worksheets as above, it is a small step to knowing the ten times table.

A useful way of practising this is with money. Saving money often appeals to the young. Children at home often have a money box or collecting box and this could be instituted in school also. If one was kept only for ten pence pieces, the checking of the money would be good practice.

As the coins were posted back the pupils could check the amount in the box a coin at a time, 'one ten is ten, two tens are twenty'. . . . The money may have to be checked and rechecked in different ways by turning it out again on the table and counting the number of coins.

Checking the money should not just be an academic exercise. There are many occasions to check how much money there is in the kitty.

How many fingers and how many toes?

A lighthearted game can be played by lining up sets of pupils, perhaps all the boys or all the girls or those in blue or those with fair hair. Let the rest guess how many fingers the set has between them.

Note how they tackle this problem. Do they count the fingers one by one? Do they count the number of children and then say five tens are fifty, or do they count along the row in tens?

Let them talk about the quickest way to find the answer.

Let them play the same game with toes which cannot be touched and counted one by one.

Number strips

Pupils can now add to their unit strip and make a tens strip with squared paper with two squares for each numeral:

| 1 0 | 2 0 | 3 0 | 4 0 | 5 0 | 6 0 | 7 0 | 8 0 | 9 0 | 100 |

One of these could be mounted on the wall so that the teacher can point to a number (say ten) and ask questions. Ten and ten more are? Fifty and ten more? Thirty and ten less? Pupils can be shown how to use their strips as calculators in this way by moving their finger backwards or forwards along the line.

Action and language
An important milestone has been reached with the understanding of tens and units. Many activities should be chosen that lead to this understanding. Pupils now are used to sorting a small number of objects (beads, bricks, pencils, sticks, straws) into sets of ten (bundles, boxes, strings, bags). Keep the number of objects within limits (twenty to thirty) at first. Encourage them to place the complete bundles on the left-hand side and the remainder on the right. Let them tell you how many objects they have when they have sorted them. Note the method of counting: no method is wrong if the result is right but some methods are very slow and possibly inaccurate. Give the pupils a chance to experiment and make suggestions. Encourage those who come up with a quick method of counting, for example bundles first, ten, twenty and then the loose sticks counted on, twenty-one, twenty-two. Your pupils will almost certainly need plenty of practice with a variety of materials at this stage.

Try to ensure that they are counting for some *purpose* and that they can see the reason for knowing how many pencils or straws there are.

If such purposeful counting does not provide enough practice, then games and competitions can be added.

If pupils are encouraged to speed up they will begin to use an efficient method of counting. A ping timer is often useful so that pupils can time themselves and beat their own record.

Bring me . . .
The game should now be reversed and a pile of bundles and loose sticks spread out on the table. The teacher asks the group to, 'Bring me thirty-two,' and so on. Children could be asked to do this in turn, or it could be made into a race. Pupils who are still counting out one at a time will be likely to come last and

should be encouraged to count in tens instead. As competence increases larger numbers can be used up to forty, fifty or beyond.

Pictures and patterns
Pictures can now be used instead of real objects. Flash cards can be prepared with sets of ten and some over. Small groups could organise their own flash card game with some encouragement and spot checks from the teacher. Here are some examples of cards:

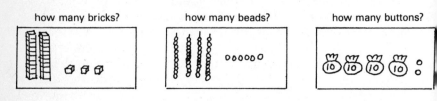

how many bricks?   how many beads?   how many buttons?

Recording results with pictures and symbols
Pupils will now be ready to record their results. They can be shown how to record the number of bundles first (two) and then loose bricks (3) to make the number 23. Using their number strips of tens and some spare unit cards they can be shown how to place a unit card over the nought to make 20 into 23, or forty into 49, for instance.

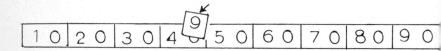

1 0 | 2 0 | 3 0 | 4 9 | 5 0 | 6 0 | 7 0 | 8 0 | 9 0

Pairs of pupils can test each other's ability using the number strip and spare digits. One calls out any number between ten and ninety-nine and the other covers a nought on the strip to make the correct number. If the number called out is a multiple of ten, then the nought does not have to be covered, of course.

Their ability to do this should be the subject of spot checks and then they can graduate to writing down the number that is called out instead of making it on the number strip.

Individual worksheets can also be duplicated for desk top work.

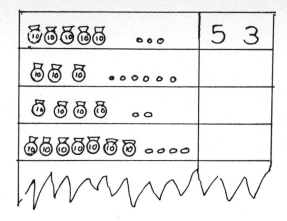

Games to play

PELMANISM OR PAIRS

Pairs of numbered cards are prepared using Waddington's blank playing cards. The numbers ten to ninety-nine can be stencilled on the cards or letraset numbers can be used. The cards, like playing cards, should be able to be 'read' either way up as follows: You will have too many pairs of cards to play with for one game and they should be divided up into sets of twenty pairs at the most. The rules are the same as for any other game of pelmanism except that to claim a pair of cards the player has to be able to read them correctly.

TENS AND UNITS SNAP

This is played with duplicate cards as above, except that four cards will be needed for each value instead of two. Again, not all the sets of four can be in play at the same time as there would be too many for comfort. It is played like the conventional game of Snap except that instead of calling out 'Snap' when you spot two cards alike, you have to call out the value of the cards (fifty-six) in order to claim them.

BINGO

There are many Bingo games on the market and they are particularly useful for place value recognition if pupils take it in turn to be the caller.

Using money

Materials
Real coins (10p and 1p and 2p). A money box.

A handful of 10 pence and 1 penny coins can be totted up by posting them into the money box using the 10 pence coins first and counting in tens, and then adding on the 1 penny coins. For example: ten, twenty, thirty, forty, fifty; fifty-one, fifty-two, fifty-three, fifty-four. To start with, make the number of 1 penny coins less than ten. The more able pupils will be ready to cope with 2 pence pieces also. The coins can alternatively be counted by laying them out in rows and keeping all the silver coins on the left-hand side and the coppers on the right.

Worksheets can be duplicated using coin rubber stamps (Philograph Publications Ltd.) The pupils must fill in the total for each line.

MONEY CHANGING GAME (twenty pence)

Materials
A coin card for each pupil (see below), a dice and shaker. A kitty of ten pence and one penny coins.

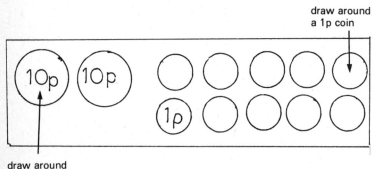

To play
Each player in turn throws the dice, collects the appropriate number of one penny coins from the kitty and places them in the spaces provided on the card. When ten spaces have been covered the coppers are returned to the kitty and exchanged for

a silver piece which is placed in the space on the left. The first player to collect exactly twenty pence is the winner.

The same game can be played with a target of 30, 40 or 50 pence. Avoid a version which takes too long for the attention span of the particular pupils.

MONEY CHANGING TOWERS
A similar game called 'Money Changing Towers' is described in the book *Let's Join In* which is published by Souvenir Press.

A grown-up will probably have to teach the game in the first place to an individual pupil, but when they have learnt, pupils can play together in small groups or in pairs. If the groups are too large and players have to wait a long time for their turn to come round, they may lose interest.

Number squares
Pupils can now begin to add to their number strips and build up a complete number square as follows.

Materials
A sheet of squared paper for each pupil (10 mm squares or larger) or the first page of their exercise book.

A ten by ten square is edged in and ideally the numerals are filled in by the pupils. This should not be done all at once. The first line can be completed by pupils who are only familiar with single numbers, the second line by those who are familiar with the 'teens'. The sheet should be kept handy for reference (when completed it could be backed with card and covered with transparent library film).

A large version on the wall can be used for group work. Encourage pupils to talk about their number sheet—for example, to find the multiples of ten underneath one another, or to discover columns when counting in twos or fives. Duplicate sheets could be used to colour these in or to discover the pattern which emerges when every ninth number is coloured in or every eleventh number.

Show the pupils how their squares can be used for adding (counting on) and subtracting (counting back) also.

(Scholar's counting and number boards similar to that overleaf can be ordered from Philip and Tacey Ltd. and come in packs of

1	2	3	4	5	6	7	8	9	10
11	12	13	14	15	16	17	18	19	20
21	22	23	24	25	26	27	28	29	30
31	32	33	34	35	36	37	38	39	40
41	42	43	44	45	46	47	48	49	50
51	52	53	54	55	56	57	58	59	60
61	62	63	64	65	66	67	68	69	70
71	72	73	74	75	76	77	78	79	80
81	82	83	84	85	86	87	88	89	90
91	92	93	94	95	96	97	98	99	100

Introduce this gradually, first thirty squares, then forty and then fifty and so on.

25. *On the reverse side is a square table chart which can be used for multiplication and division.)*

ADDITION OF TENS AND UNITS WITHOUT CARRYING

Materials
Coins 10p and 1p, coin rubber stamps 10p and 1p, unifix cubes, beads, beans, buttons, etc., with bags and rubber bands.

HOW MUCH MONEY HAVE WE GOT BETWEEN US?
Start with a practical activity of adding up combined resources

to find if they are enough for a desired purchase. Encourage a systematic arrangement of coins with the 10p coins on the left as follows:

John's money

Mary's money

Pupils should by now be well able to check their own money by counting on: ten, twenty, twenty-one, twenty-two, twenty-three pence.

They can then count the two rows of coins together: ten, twenty, thirty, forty, fifty, fifty-one, fifty-two, fifty-three, fifty-four, fifty-five.

After practice with the actual coins, workcards using the coin stamps can be made and the total can be printed in figures by the pupils under the array. Further practice using unifix cubes or bags of buttons or sticks and bands should be undertaken. Only when the pupils are confident and accurate in dealing with real objects should conventional addition sums be introduced. Check that the pupils can read the numbers correctly and know what + means.

ADDITION OF TENS AND UNITS WITH CARRYING

In order to understand the process involved in the addition of tens and units with carrying, your pupils will need much practice in changing ten units into one ten, twenty into two tens and thirty into three tens. The practice should be varied and sticks, counters, unifix cubes, beads and coins can all be used. The process is the same whatever the materials.

CHANGING COINS

Materials
Coins (10p and 1p) and a container.

Each pupil is given a pile of one penny coins and the pool of ten pence coins is placed in the middle of the table.

The task is to count out the one penny coins into piles of ten and then to change them for ten pence coins from the pool. When all their coins have been counted out they read how many they have got: 'ten, twenty, thirty, forty, forty-one, forty-two, forty-three.' They then write down the total, 43. They are then handed some more one penny coins (enough to make another ten with some over) and they then change these coins. *Talk* about it: 'You had forty-three pence and then added nine more and that made fifty-two.'

When the pupils are practically adept at changing money and calculating the total, they can work from workcards.

Start with the easier task of adding units only to the tens and units. This should be practised with many different materials.

Using the number squares
The number squares can be used for extra practice in addition: either the twenty, thirty, forty, fifty or a hundred square.

A pupil chooses any number in the square—for example, 24—and then chooses another number on the first line—say, seven. He points to the 24 in his square and then counts on seven more to reach 31.

Pupils can be left to make their own sums and record their answers in their books (this is more creative than being given a page of sums to complete). The sums can be recorded as 24 + 7 = 31 or as follows:

The wall-hung number square enables the teacher to demonstrate to a group and the pupils to take turns to find the answers to her questions, for example: 'How many is fifty-seven and seven more?'

Subtraction should go hand in hand with addition, and pupils should practise sixty-four and seven less alongside the addition sum so that it becomes obvious that if fifty-seven and seven more is the same as sixty-four, then sixty-four and seven less must be fifty-seven.

SQUARE GAME

Materials
A number square (30, 50 or 100), dice and thrower, counters.

To play
The number square is placed on the table to serve as a board. Players throw the dice in turn and, starting at number one, move their counters the appropriate number of squares forward. The first player to reach the end of the board exactly is the winner. This game encourages counting on and guessing what square you will land on next.

A more advanced version lets each player throw two dice and add up the two face values before counting on from the square he was on at the last turn. The more able can be encouraged to describe their move: 'I am on forty-five; forty-five and nine more will be fifty-four.'

Another version of the game, to give practice in adding on tens to tens and units, would be to colour in some of the squares. If a player lands on a coloured square he can move forward ten places. The more able pupils will see that they need not count on 'ten' along the board, but can move *down* one to add ten to a number, for instance 82 is under 72 on the board.

Written work on the addition of tens and units

Materials
Structured apparatus such as unifix cubes; loose rods and bundles of ten rods; bags holding ten counters and loose counters; strings of ten beads and loose beads. Worksheets, flash cards of numerals over 10, for example 13, 51, 60, 78.

Procedure
Each pupil is provided with one set of structured material. At another session the pupils change materials with one another.

Warm up
A group of pupils watch while you hold up a card, say, 35. Pupils see who can be first to lay out their apparatus appropriately:

Alternate with the teacher putting out an array of structural materials and the pupils saying how many are there and writing it down in their books.

The pupils can then be invited to arrange any number of sticks and loose cubes out of their collection and write down the number they have selected in figures, for example 56.

They can then choose another arrangement and write that down until they have shown their mastery.

Now they should arrange their sticks and cubes in two rows and read whatever sum they have written, that is, $32 + 24 = 56$

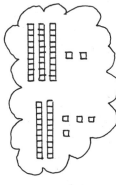

(see left). Cover the bottom row and see whether they can tell you how many are left when 24 is taken away from 56. As pupils are left free to make up their own sums, it will sometimes happen that the number of units exceeds ten and will have to be carried over into the tens collection. Making their own sums in this way will lead to greater understanding than being given rows of figures to be totted up mechanically. However, once they have mastered the rules the pupils can be encouraged to record their own sums in the conventional manner:

$$
\begin{array}{r}
7\,2 \\
9 \\
\hline
8\,1
\end{array}
$$

In an integrated setting, where pupils may need to conform to the established pattern, the teacher can now make out worksheets of sums which can be calculated with the use of structural materials or with the use of the number squares.

Use of calculators

Once a pupil shows he understands what he is doing when adding or subtracting numbers and also is familiar with the plus (+) and minus (−) and equals (=) signs, then a case can be made for the use of pocket calculators. The important thing is *how* they are used; their use at this stage will not help a pupil to understand what he is doing but will enable him to check results which he has arrived at independently. This independent ability to check results is important for older pupils especially, who are often over-dependent upon parents and teachers.

Calculators are also very handy when we are inculcating self-help skills of shopping, checking change, keeping accounts, measuring amounts and so on.

By this time, pupils have been encouraged to count in twos, fives, fours and tens, but this ability does not guarantee that they *understand* the concept that five times two is the same as ten ($5 \times 2 = 10$), or that is another way of stating that two and two and two and two and two is the same as ten ($2 + 2 + 2 + 2 + 2 = 10$). To make this connection they may require further active practice in counting pairs of objects (gloves, socks, shoes, boots, legs, eyes, ears, knitting needles), and in putting these actions into words—for example, 'six pairs of knitting needles is the same as twelve knitting needles.' They will need both to handle real objects and to see them represented in pictures or patterns before being able to understand the numerical symbols on their own. Colouring the even numbers on their number square will help to bridge the gap between counting in twos and recognising the appropriate numerals. When this stage has been reached, the more conventional two times table can be put up on the wall, with pictorial reminders.

$$1 \times 2 = 2$$
$$2 \times 2 = 4$$
$$3 \times 2 = 6$$
$$4 \times 2 = 8$$
$$5 \times 2 = 10$$
$$6 \times 2 = 12$$

The class can read this table out together—one times two is two, two times two is four, and so on. The chart can then be used for solving practical problems: how many knitting needles shall we need for six pupils? Or, how many chopsticks for four people coming to a Chinese meal? Or else the other way round: we have 14 knitting needles, how many pairs is that?

There is no need to write out the whole table at first, and nowadays ten times two is probably as far as we need to go.

Five times table
Counting in fives has already been started practically, using the fingers of a hand. Pictures and rebuses can be substituted for the real thing. A five pointed star is a useful rebus.

A pictorial chart of the five times table can now go on the wall, with stick-on stars as a reminder. This chart can be read by the class: five times one is five, five times two is ten . . .

More importantly, it should be used as an aid to solve practical problems involving multiplication or division.

$$1 \times 5 = 5$$
$$2 \times 5 = 10$$
$$3 \times 5 = 15$$
$$4 \times 5 = 20$$

Only part of the table needs to be introduced at first, and it can then be gradually extended. Try covering up a final figure as shown above, and see who can give you the answer to two times five are . . . ? for instance. Eventually all the final figures can be covered over to test the pupils' knowledge. Similarly, one row can be covered so that only the final figure appears, and the question asked, 'Twenty is the same as how many times five?' When they have coloured in the fives on their own number square, this can be used as a ready reckoner when they are doing their own sums, or they could use Philip & Tacey's printed boards.

Ten times table
Pupils are now very familiar with counting in tens and counting out tens of rods, unifix blocks, beads, etc., and ten pence coins.

A ten times table can now be displayed on the wall, using a rebus of the unifix rods, or a facsimile of a ten pence coin.

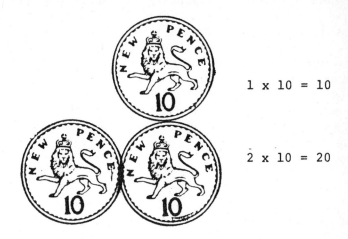

$$1 \times 10 = 10$$

$$2 \times 10 = 20$$

The answers can be covered up as before and direct questions asked: 'What is six times ten?' Similarly, the answers can be left and the rest of the line covered to answer how many times ten is eighty, etc.

Again, the number squares with the tens coloured in can be used as a ready reckoner. Shopping, or planning the cost of a number of items at ten pence each, or of ten items at, say, eight pence each, gives additional practice.

Three and four times tables
Counting in threes and fours has already been introduced, using four-legged animals and tables and chairs and the sides of rectangles to illustrate the four-times table, and sides of triangles and clover leaves to illustrate the three times. The actual table charts, with illustrations or rebuses, should now be displayed and practice given with these as above.

Six times table
Nowadays, on account of our decimal currency, this table no longer has such a high priority. However, many people still measure in inches and feet and a six-inch measure comes in

handy. Also, goods are still sold in dozens and half-dozens, and most of us have a twelve-hour clock.

Dice can be used for a game to familiarise the students with counting in sixes. The rule of the game is that turns are taken in throwing the dice, but a player only scores when a six is thrown. Each player keeps a record of how many sixes he has scored, and then the table chart is used to find out who has won the game.

Tom scored three sixes and $3 \times 6 = 18$
John scored two sixes and $2 \times 6 = 12$
Mary scored five sixes and $5 \times 6 = 30$

Who won the game?

Eggs are still sold by the dozen, and egg boxes conveniently have six compartments. Closed egg boxes could be used to test a student's ability to tell how many eggs there will be in, say, eight boxes. He can check by counting the compartments or putting ping-pong balls inside. This ability is of practical value as preparation for a cookery lesson, for calculating how many boxes will be needed for the whole class, for instance.

A table chart should be mounted on the wall as before, and practice given in memorising the table or part of it.

Seven times table
This is one of the hardest tables to memorise and one which is not very frequently used. However, there are seven days in the week and you may feel that it would be useful to make a start on this table. It is probably best introduced in a practical context, when timetables and TV programmes are an issue, and this will be dealt with in Chapter 15.

Other tables
There is no point in memorising tables just for the sake of doing so, and the eight and twelve times tables could well be left for later. The nine times should be coloured in, and also the eleven times.

To many of the older generation, learning about fractions—or vulgar fractions—was either a nightmare or an intellectual exercise. Vague memories of which part of a fraction is the numerator and which the denominator; of finding the lcm (lowest common multiple) and hcf (highest common factor) may linger on, but how many times since leaving school have you had 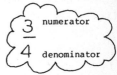 to remember the rules for adding, subtracting, multiplying or dividing vulgar fractions?

Although decimal fractions have now superseded vulgar fractions for difficult calculations, we do still need some knowledge of fractions to cope with daily living. We need to know how to cut an apple in half so that each person has an equal share, or how to find a quarter of a pound. When telling the time we must understand the meaning of half past, a quarter past, and a quarter to. In cookery we may need to measure out a quarter of a pint. In this chapter we shall introduce the most common fractions in a practical setting.

As before, the ALPS sequence will be followed, and active experience will be accompanied with the language of that experience. Pictorial representation will follow and when the basic concepts have been grasped the notation can be introduced.

Practical introduction
When introducing fractions it is important to remember always to relate the part to the whole: not to refer to a quarter but a quarter of an apple or of a cake.

The idea of 'a half' should be familiar from early on if attention is always drawn to the fact that when sharing out apples or cakes or tarts, we often have to cut each apple, etc., in half. If cutting in half is also referred to as cutting in two pieces, this will lay the foundation for the later introduction of notation—a half is one whole divided into two or $\frac{1}{2}$. It is important that children should actively experience halving apples, cakes, etc. themselves, and that after demonstration they should all frequently have a turn.

start with food!

Paper folding

First-hand experience of halving and quartering is gained by folding. In the craft lesson, accurate folding of a piece of paper in half to create a Christmas or birthday card will make a beginning. Practice in folding circles of paper in half and then in quarters can be part of a craft lesson in making paper doilies.

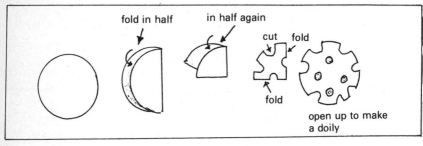

fold in half   in half again   cut   fold   fold   open up to make a doily

Making paper rings of dancing children will give further practice in folding and should also prove a talking point.

Cut out a rectangle of paper and fold it in half and then in half again as shown below. Cut out the dancers as shown. Let everybody make some. Talk about folding in half and then in half again to make four quarters.

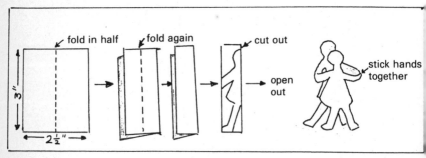

fold in half   fold again   cut out   open out   stick hands together
3"   2½"

Someone may notice that although you made four quarters there are only two dancers. How was that? You might then use a strip of paper twice as long and give another fold so that it is folded into eight pieces, or eighths. How come that there are only four dancers?

More fractions with folding

MAKING A ZIGZAG BOOK

We saw how a piece of paper can be folded in half to make a birthday card or the page of a little reading book, for instance.

By zigzag folding other fractions can be demonstrated, and the result is a useful little book or album for snaps.

This will take a little more preparation on your part. Decide how many pages to begin with and then measure out a strip of paper three times the width of a page, if you are introducing thirds, or four times the width for quarters. Mark the first fold and then fold along the strip in zigzag fashion. The illustration below is of sixths. Make sure everyone knows there will be six pages and that each page is a sixth of the whole book. If you made cardboard covers to the book (5mm bigger than a page), you would have a durable little album which could then be decorated on the cover.

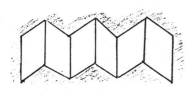

As an introduction to sevenths, a handy pocket timetable could be made in this way. The highlights of each weekday could be illustrated on the pages for reference (swimming, perhaps, or cookery lessons).

FRACTIONS WITH CIRCLES

When we come to telling the time we need to be familiar with the visual image of half of a circle (half an hour) and a quarter of a circle (a quarter of an hour).

Begin by providing circular pieces of paper which can be folded in half. If the edges are stuck together they will make little bags for sweets in the school shop or witches' hats for Hallowe'en.

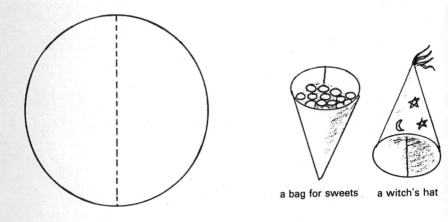

a bag for sweets   a witch's hat

MORE SIXTHS: MAKING A TWIZZLER

Materials
Stout card, felt-tipped pens, thin nylon string, pair of compasses.

To make
Set your compasses at 1½ ins and draw a circle on the card. If the card is not very stiff, draw and cut out two circles and stick them together. Keeping your compass set, mark off the outside of the circle as shown opposite. This will divide the edge of your circle exactly into six. Join the marks on the edge of the circle by ruling lines through the centre.

Colour each segment in bright colours.

Pierce two small holes about an eighth of an inch from the centre and thread the string through. Tie the two ends of the string together.

To use

Put your fingers into the two loops of string. Hold one hand still and twist the string round with the other hand. When the string is well twisted, pull gently in and out with both hands and the twizzler will rotate.

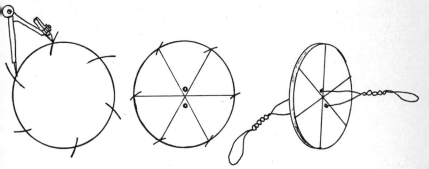

A SPINNING TOP

To make

Make as for the twizzler, but rule lines between the outside marks on the edge of the circle and cut along these lines. Paint the six sections in bright colours and number them. Make a small hole in the centre of the top and push the stub of a pencil through.

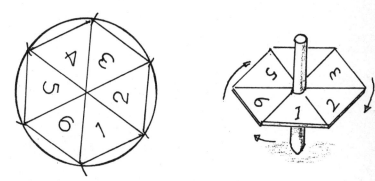

Not only is this spinning top useful for playing the number games described in this volume, but in making and using it the teacher can familiarise the players with the correct naming of the segments as sixths. She could perhaps suggest that one sixth should be coloured red and another sixth blue. The players could be encouraged as describe how they were colouring their own tops—for example, 'I've made one sixth green.'

The colouring of the twizzler can also be described in this way. Twizzlers and tops can also be made divided into eight segments to introduce eighths.

Pictorial representations

In order to consolidate the knowledge of fractions gained by the activities described above, some pictorial representations of common fractions can now be cut out and drawn and kept in a folder or book for handy reference. If these fractions can all be recognised and named, then the notation can also be included at this stage.

HALVES AND QUARTERS

Halves and quarters can be cut out of circles of coloured paper and stuck into the book and labelled. These can also be illustrated with folded strips of coloured paper, but these should not be cut off the strip.

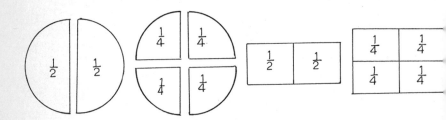

See how many of these fractions can be spotted and named—on the clock, a half-moon in the sky, a piece of cake, half a bar of chocolate.

Making patterns

Other fractions can be introduced in the form of patterns to be coloured in.

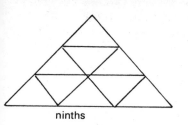

ninths

eighths

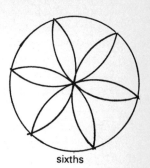

sixths

Use of fractions

Practice in folding paper in order to divide it in half, and in folding laundry as well, leads to the realisation of the practical use of this folding technique for finding the middle of a piece of wood, for instance, to saw it into two equal lengths. Take a strip of paper the length of the piece of wood and fold it exactly in half and then use it as a measure. A length of string can be used in a similar way if the middle point is marked with a pen.

In cookery lessons, simple pictorial recipes can be followed to increase the independence of the older pupils. Pupils will need to know how to measure out half a block of butter or margarine, and they can mark the middle point of the block in this way then cut. Similarly with a quarter of a block.

half a block of butter

James Hargreaves' excellent book, *Cookery for Handicapped People*, has detailed suggestions for helping handicapped people to follow recipes and become independent. The recipes are mainly pictorial but the recognition of the notations of ½, ¼ and ¾ is a help in following them.

Telling the time

A start can be made in telling the time from the minute hand on a conventional clock. Half an hour and a quarter of an hour can now be recognised, and so lead to the recognition of half past, a quarter past and a quarter to the hour. More on telling the time will be included in Chapter 15.

Harder problems with fractions

So far we have considered fractions as involving parts of one whole thing: finding half of an hour or a quarter of a block of margarine, for instance. In real life problems arise when we need to know how many ounces there are in a quarter of a pound, or how many inches in a third of a foot.

In order to understand these problems we need to discover the logic behind the notation of fractions—for example, that the two at the bottom of $\frac{1}{2}$ means that it is shared equally between two, or that the six at the bottom of $\frac{1}{6}$ means that it is shared equally between six. It may take some time and practice with well known fractions before the idea is fully established, but once the relationship between fractions and equal division is established, the harder problems can be tackled.

Active visual demonstrations will help to make the solving of these more understandable. For instance, if we want to find how many ounces there are in half a pound, we need to know that there are sixteen in one pound. (We have used pounds and ounces as an example, but this can be translated into metric measures.) Using squared paper, a number strip is printed on both sides, sixteen squares long. This is then folded in half very carefully, so that there are eight numbers on one side of the fold and eight on the other.

| 1 | 2 | 3 | 4 | 5 | 6 | 7 | 8 | 9 | 10 | 11 | 12 | 13 | 14 | 15 | 16 |

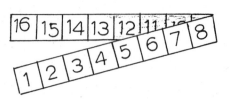

Do not be in a hurry to move on. Let your pupils have some fun making their own strips of different lengths and then guessing what half of that number will be, or how many will be on either side of the middle fold. Do not worry if some of them choose an uneven number to divide in half, for example, 13. They will discover that there are twelve squares and 'a bit' on either side of the middle, and this can be tackled later on, when they are more proficient.

Vary the practical exercises with halves. Give your pupils a number of counters, for instance, to divide in half, and let them draw a circle or square to enclose each set. Again, give them time to experiment with any number they choose. A great deal of learning can take place during this simple activity. Some pupils, of course, may find they do not have to share out the counters or fold the paper strip, but know the answer straight away.

Do not go on to finding quarters until they are pretty slick with the halves. Quarters can be found by folding also, or, to make it more fun, four 'ponds' or enclosures can be drawn on a sheet for the four equal sets.

Encourage pupils to invent their own stories—for example, the farmer had twelve hens but only four hen-houses. Each house was the same size and housed the same number of hens, so how many hens would there be in each house?

With prompting, the children will produce their own ideas, though perhaps not as fluently, for example, 'Mine are pigs!' The more they enter into and talk about the story, the more likely they are to understand what half of eight is, or a quarter of sixteen. In due course other fractions can be introduced in similar activities. With the teacher's guidance this should lead to the realisation that $\frac{1}{4}$ is just another way of expressing 'one divided by four', or 'one shared equally into four parts'.

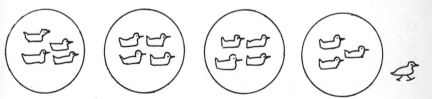

'Mine are ducks in ponds . . . one hasn't gone in yet!'

Language
Middle, centre, fold, half, quarter, third, fifth, sixth, equal, the same, different, more, less, divide, share out, shorter, longer.

The list of new words reflects the new concepts which are needed for the understanding of fractions. It is pointless to proceed with written work until these concepts are established and most of the terms understood.

Symbols or notation of problems
When this stage of understanding has been reached, worksheets with fractions can be tackled relatively independently, using the number strips and enclosures to help work them out.

Here are a few suggestions:

$\frac{1}{2}$ of 8
$\frac{1}{2}$ of 14
$\frac{1}{4}$ of 20
$\frac{1}{3}$ of 9
$\frac{1}{3}$ of 12
$\frac{1}{5}$ of 15
$\frac{1}{5}$ of 25
$\frac{1}{6}$ of 12
$\frac{1}{6}$ of 24

First check that they know what to do when the problems are given to them orally, for example, 'Find a half of sixteen or a quarter of twelve.' If they fumble with these problems or get many of them wrong, they are not yet ready for this kind of written work and need more time with practical activities.

Section Four

MEASURING AND SHOPPING

Even when they are adults, some people seem to have no idea of time. They are always being late and cannot remember what they did the day before. Young babies seem literally to have no idea of time. They live for the moment, and out of sight is out of mind. The difficult notion of the passing of time, of yesterday, today and tomorrow, develops slowly and gradually. Small children cannot understand when told to 'wait a minute', but become very restless if their wants are not immediately met.

As adults we are constantly referring to the passage of time—'Put your coat on before you go out to play,' or, 'Clean your teeth after lunch.' Make sure your child understands these directions before assuming that he is being disobedient because he is not following them A child needs to learn the ordered sequence of events before learning about the way we measure time, in seconds, minutes, hours, days, months and years. It is quite a tall order, and if the child has additional learning difficulties or is very immature, this ability will be slow to develop. Only by careful observation and regular checks can we tailor our demands to his level of understanding.

Sequencing
Can your child follow a sequence of two instructions such as 'Hang your coat up and then come in,' 'The boys are to get in line first and then the girls,' or 'Wash your hands and sit down'? Observe carefully what he does: immature children will only remember the last part of the instruction they have heard and so will get the sequencing wrong.

Can some of the children follow a three-'bit' sequence such as, 'Put some paper down, take your shoes off and give them a brush,' or 'Paint with the red, then wash your brush and paint with the blue'?

In *Pathways to Independence* by Jeffree and Cheseldine (Hodder & Stoughton) you will find a checklist of the developmental sequence of the concept of time, starting in early infancy with the development of a regular sleeping/waking pattern, progressing to the ability to anticipate some daily events such as meal times, or showing an appreciation of the difference between weekdays and the weekend by their behaviour on getting up in the morning, and understanding the difference between today, tomorrow and yesterday.

MEASURING TIME

It is much harder to measure the passing of time than it is to measure length or weight. For one thing, it does not stand still to be measured, and if you get it wrong you cannot go back to the start and measure again. Then you can measure length with a unit of length held up against it, or weight by balancing units of weight against what is to be measured. Not so with time. No one can pick up a unit of time and use it as a measure. Time has to be measured against something else—the distance a hand has gone round a clock, or the volume of sand that has fallen through an egg timer.

Liebeck (1984) suggests that we should start children off by measuring with a metronome, pendulum or loudly ticking clock, so that the intervals can be either seen or heard. By altering the swing of the pendulum or metronome children can experience a fast or slow rhythm. They can then count in time with the swings, or in the playground they can count in time with a child skipping. They can learn to 'time' one another performing various tasks—for example, 'Mary took twelve ticks to change her shoes and David took twenty ticks.' Many examples of timing of tasks will be needed to establish the idea of David taking a 'longer time' than Mary who took a 'shorter time'. We can also say that Mary was quicker than David who took more time to complete the task and was slower.

People who 'take all day' to complete a simple task are also said to have 'no idea of time'. We may find that some of our pupils are like this: they may get there in the end but have no sense of urgency. If this becomes a habit these children may 'miss the boat', because other people cannot wait and tend to get impatient and complete tasks for them.

AN EGG TIMER OR PING TIMER

If a timer is introduced, pupils can pace themselves on various tasks and try to 'beat the clock', or rather 'beat the timer'. This will also sharpen their sense of the passage of time and help them to stay alert. A stop-watch might also be used, and this makes a good introduction to telling the time on a watch or clock.

TELLING THE TIME

Take every opportunity to establish the ability to recount events in sequence: What did you do first this morning? And after that? Retelling simple stories in their proper sequence will be a regular event. Beware of too many changes in plan during the course of the day and try to establish a routine.

Highlights of the day

Most children look forward to certain highlights of their day. Discuss with them what these are. Is it lunch time, play time, home time, teatime or bedtime? For some it may be listening to a special programme on the radio or television.

Make a big cardboard clockface for the classroom or playroom at home. Cut out an hour hand in stiff card and fix it to the centre with a split pin paper fastener so that it will move round.

Let everyone have a go at moving the hand round the clock saying the hours as they go: 'One o'clock, two o'clock, three o'clock . . .' Make sure that nobody tries to turn the clock back! A few minutes' informal practice every day can then follow, during which pupils in turn put the hour hand at six o'clock or nine o'clock.

It is useful to turn this session into a discussion in which everyone joins. What time does Peter get up? or go to bed? What do you watch on telly? Do you know what time it is on? Perhaps we could look it up in the *Radio Times* or *TV Times*. Following this someone could choose a very special time of the day and the hour hand could be set at this time—perhaps three o'clock when we are getting ready to go home. The pupils should then be shown the hour hand on the real classroom clock and watch out for when this reaches three also, so that they can tell when it is time to pack up.

On another day, snack time could be chosen, or lunch time. If a cuckoo clock could be acquired this would make telling the time easier by counting the 'cuckoos'. Duplicated sheets of clockfaces can be handed round for filling in different times by drawing the hour hand.

Not all the highlights of the day take place in school hours, and when their children are learning to read the hours, parents might well instal a cardboard clockface at home and set the hour hand for when Daddy comes home or for a favourite programme or for bedtime.

Half hours and quarter hours
Create opportunities for pupils to check the time on the real clock by looking at where the little hand is pointing, and when they are really competent at this you can introduce half and quarter hours.

If they have had practice with fractions they will be familiar with the shape of half a circle and a quarter of a circle and be able to name these parts. Draw a circle the same size as the cardboard clock on a piece of coloured tissue paper or coloured cellophane. Cut the circle in half and lay it over the clock face so that the hours are visible underneath. Make sure everyone knows where the hour hand is pointing and demonstrate that it is now half past the hour as shown by the large hand.

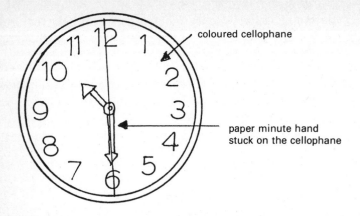

coloured cellophane

paper minute hand
stuck on the cellophane

As before, daily practice is needed for all to be able to read the time correctly, for example half past six, half past nine, and so on.

On their duplicated clockfaces the pupils could now draw in the hour hand and the minute hand to indicate the times of events in the day.

They should be encouraged to watch the real clock and tell the teacher when it is half past the hour. This can be followed by timing half an hour on the clock when cooking, for instance the time it takes for the minute hand to complete a semi-circle (the coloured half of the clock.) The next period of time to introduce is quarter of an hour and this too can be cut out in cellophane. The pupils can then learn to read a quarter past the hour.

A QUARTER TO ONE
The quarter circle of cellophane can also be used to demonstrate a quarter *to* the hour, but this concept is considerably more difficult than a quarter past.

Minutes
An ability to count up to 60 and to count in fives up to 60 should precede the introduction of minutes.

Remember that minutes past the hour are easier to learn than minutes to the hour and should be tackled first. Telling the time is not easy, especially as clocks differ and some have

Roman numerals and some have no numerals at all. To a certain extent digital watches make it easier to tell the time, but remember that they teach nothing about the passing of time which can be experienced by watching the hands go round or the sand flow in an egg timer. The numerals are also fairly difficult to read and a child needs to be able to read numerals from one to sixty in order to be able to tell the time.

DIFFERENT TYPES OF TIMEPIECES

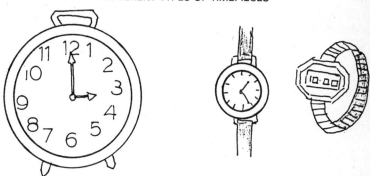

Language
Late, later, early, earlier, time, half past, a quarter to, a long time, a short time, time for, what time is it, minutes, seconds, hours, long hand, short hand, fast, slow, clock, watch.

Timing
I have suggested that children should get used to using an egg timer or stop-watch or alarm clock to pace or time their performance on a task. The cookery lesson also provides opportunities to make sure that whatever is cooked is not under- or overdone. Begin with timing a boiled egg (hard boiled) for the salad using an egg timer. A ping timer can be used for cakes in the oven or for timing potatoes on the boil.

If the need arises for reading timetables, perhaps for catching a bus for a journey to a college of further education, then this should be taught in that particular context. Similarly, a simple timetable can be drawn out showing the time of one or two important events in the day (going to the swimming baths, for instance, or a special programme on the television either at home or in school). It is best to start with one item per day and to choose one where getting the time right is important. Let one pupil be responsible for watching the time.

THE DAYS OF THE WEEK
Parents of children with severe learning difficulties sometimes avoid talking about what is going to happen tomorrow because their child keeps pestering them and asking, 'Is it tomorrow yet?'

As I have said, the small baby lives only in the present, and it is a gradual process to become aware of the past and the future. When the time is ripe parents are in the best position to foster this awareness as they not only share the day-to-day experiences of their child but have done so since babyhood. Barbara Tizard found that, no doubt for this reason, parents *do* talk more of the past and future to their children than do teachers in nursery school. It is through sharing these experiences and talking about them that a child begins to appreciate the passing of time.

Parents should talk to their children about the events of yesterday, today and tomorrow when they are old enough to remember going to Auntie Nell or buying some new shoes. It is a good thing to prepare for an event the day before: 'Tomorrow we are going to the zoo.' Perhaps the model animals could be got out so that the child anticipates what he is going to see. On the day of the outing the child can be reminded of the toy animals he looked at yesterday: 'That is an elephant like the one we looked at yesterday.' If a permanent record of the outing in the way of mementos or drawing is then put into a book, this makes a good focus for a discussion of the past.

Over the years parents have evolved simple ways of getting children to realise what is meant by 'tomorrow'. 'It will be after you have gone to sleep and when you wake up in the morning.' Your child will need time before he is able to project himself far into the future or wait patiently for a birthday which is months ahead. Even waiting a few days may prove difficult at first.

Notice whether your child seems to differentiate between weekdays and weekends. Even before he starts school these are likely to be very different. The family is likely to be together at weekends, for instance. If he puts on different clothes or gets up earlier at the weekends, you will know by his behaviour that he is noticing the difference. Now is the time to begin to tell him about the days of the week.

Zigzag book

An ordered weekly routine helps your child to distinguish between the seven days of the week e.g. washing on Monday, baking on Tuesday and so on. Let him make a zigzag book with a page for each day and a picture on each page.

TO MAKE THE BOOK

Cut a strip of paper 54 cms (21 ins) long and fold it in a zigzag to make seven pages. Print the days of the week in order on the top of each page and let your child draw a picture showing a highlight of each day. Let him draw one picture at a time, the Monday picture on Monday and so on.

This is something he can do at home and it can be made a useful talking point: 'It's Tuesday today, what did you do today? What did you do yesterday? What day of the week was it yesterday? What shall we do tomorrow? What day of the week will that be?' The book can be opened out into a strip and the days of the week recited in the right order, or the pages can be folded back so that only one page is showing and the game is to guess what the next weekday will be.

When a child starts school a zigzag book can serve as a reminder of the regular important events on each day (only one per page at first), for example, Monday . . . swimming, Tuesday . . . minibus and so on.

Some schools have a weekly menu, and pupils could make a pictorial menu in their zigzag books. Most children are interested in their food and checking up on the day of the week and what you are going to have for dinner helps to make it memorable.

Several of these simple zigzag books can be made so that they form a pictorial diary. If the pages are halved, the second half can be coloured dark blue to show the night, perhaps decorated with stars. You can show your child that two weeks together make fourteen nights, or a fortnight.

If a child is reading, he can make a little reading book of the days of the week with a caption under each picture, either of one word—perhaps 'swimming'—or a sentence, such as 'We went swimming today'.

More durable books can be made with separate cards for each day fastened together with magic tape. If the book has a cover you will have to add one extra segment.

What about a television book so as not to forget which day to watch 'Blue Peter'?

THE YEAR

Modern civilisation conspires to insulate people from the seasonal changes of the year. In centrally heated houses and cars it is possible not to feel the icy blasts of winter; fruits of the summer are on sale for most of the year and sowing and harvesting may be something we never encounter.

As parents and teachers it is up to us to keep our children in touch with the seasonal changes by drawing their attention to the falling leaves of autumn, the sprouting buds and nesting birds of spring and the opening flowers and ripening fruit of summer. Growing plants help to keep children aware of seasonal changes, as do collecting frogspawn and seeing the tadpoles and frogs develop.

Nothing can take the place of this firsthand experience.

Wall charts and pictures can be reminders of the four seasons of spring, summer, autumn and winter.

The festivals

Throughout the world the passing of the year has been marked, by people of all religions and faiths, with festivals of the seasons. Many of these seasonal festivals are no longer celebrated, and those that are, are so commercialised as to have ceased to mark the seasonal cycle. Easter eggs and chickens, for instance, appear in the shops soon after Christmas.

By celebrating these festivals in a simple but appropriate way, parents and teachers can keep children in touch with the annual cycle of the year. When celebrating Easter, Midsummer's Day, Harvest and Christmas, we can bear this in mind. Children should be encouraged to recollect, perhaps with paintings and drawings, the highlights of the four seasons of the year.

The months
When introducing the months of the year, rote learning of the names of the months—January, February, etc., will not appeal to a child's imagination. Perhaps it would be better to arouse the children's feeling first through poetry:

> January brings the snow,
> Makes our feet and fingers glow,
> February brings the rain,
> Thaws the frozen lake again.
> March brings breezes, loud and shrill,
> Stirs the dancing daffodil,
> April brings the primrose sweet,
> Scatters daisies at our feet.
> May brings flocks of pretty lambs
> Skipping round their fleecy dams.
> June brings tulips, lilies, roses,
> Fills the children's hands with posies.
> Hot July brings cooling showers,
> Apricots and gilly flowers.
> August brings the sheaves of corn
> When the harvest home is borne.
> Warm September brings the fruit,
> Sportsmen then begin to shoot.
> Fresh October brings the pheasant,
> Then to gather nuts is pleasant.
> Dull November brings the blast,
> Then the leaves are whirling fast.
> Chill December brings the sleet,
> Blazing fire and Christmas treat.

This poem could be the focus of much artwork, and a calendar with the children's illustrations—a picture of one month on each page—could be hung on the wall. Birthdays and other highlights of the month should be noted and illustrated. Children cannot take in everything at once and the inclusion of the days of the week in the calendar can be left until everyone is familiar with the names of the twelve months, the order in which they follow one another and some of the characteristics of the different months.

The date
Working out the date of an event in our head in, perhaps, a fortnight's time, is not easy and requires much prior knowledge. If he has no diary or calendar to hand, the 'man-in-the-street' may take some time to work it out and may be heard muttering a mnenomic under his breath:

> Thirty days hath September,
> April, June and November;
> All the rest have thirty-one,
> Excepting February alone,
> Which has twenty-eight days clear
> And twenty-nine in each leap year.

Even then he or she may get it wrong if calculating a fortnight from a date at the end of January.

Given time, our pupils will need an engagement calendar on the wall so that they can work out coming events. This is not easy and a start can be made by filling in birthdays as they occur. Everyone needs to know the date of their own birthday.

It is customary to ask little children, 'How old are you?' They may be able to answer this question correctly, but this does not mean that they have any idea of the meaning of age. It is a difficult concept to grasp, for it encompasses that of birth and death.

Looking back
A start can be made by looking back over personal experience. Parents are in the best position to do this, especially if they have kept a photograph album and can look at snaps of the one-year-old son or daughter, then the two-year-old, and so on up to the present day. Together you can see how much you can remember of each age. Perhaps the snaps could be taken out of the album and mixed up and then put back in chronological order. See if your son or daughter can do this. When the child has sorted out the pictures of himself you may introduce the idea of a sibling (if he has one) who is so many years older or younger. He can help you work out the sibling's age when he was four, five, six, etc. Remember to point out that if his sister or brother is older than he is, then it follows that he himself is *younger*. Mother can then talk about her own age and how much older she is than her child. Again, see if he can work out how old she was when he was two, for instance. If he is ten now, how old will he be on his next birthday?

Perhaps some family snaps could be sent to school so that the age of pupils can be compared.

Until the passing of time and ages measured in years are understood, the further complication of ages in years and months should be shelved. When out for a walk, play the game of guessing the ages of the children you meet, perhaps working out how much older or younger they are than you.

At school the pupils could do a little research: find out the ages of some of the pupils in other classes and compare their ages with their own classmates, and make some records with pictures or names in their own workbooks. Perhaps they could take some polaroid pictures and print the name and age on the bottom, using these to make up problems to solve.

Mary is . . . years older than Kate.

These cards can be used in many different ways. They can be sequenced in age order, or used for a game of snap—to win the cards you must snap two pupils of the same age—or they can be used for a game of pairs.

ARE WE THE SAME AGE?
When two eight-year-olds begin to ask questions and wonder if they are the same age, it is time to introduce years and months and show that Ann is older than John although they are both eight-year-olds, because Ann is eight years and seven months and John is only eight years and two months old.

THE DATE AND DATE OF BIRTH
By now every child will have discovered his birthday on the engagements calendar. They will all probably want to record the dates in their own personal notebooks, together with their name, address and telephone number. However, so far only the birth*day* and birth *month* are probably known, not the *year* of birth. Unless your pupils are ready for a lesson in ancient history and can understand the idea of BC and AD, I think they

will simply have to learn the convention and be able to 'read' different dates—for example, that 1989 is read as nineteen eighty-nine and not as one thousand, nine hundred and eighty-nine.

Along with their own date of birth they will want to know how to write the date. This is something they will need when writing letters and is probably best tackled in this context. The day's date could well be displayed on the classroom or bedroom wall, and it could be the pupils' responsibility to see that it is always correct. Philip and Tacey supply a combined weather chart and calendar with dates, as well as pictures of weather conditions, which can be changed daily.

Language
Old, older, eldest, young, younger, youngest, birth, birthday, Monday, Tuesday, Wednesday, Thursday, Friday, Saturday, Sunday, January, February, March, April, May, June, July, August, September, October, November, December, morning, evening, day, night, today, tomorrow, week, month, year, date, fortnight, yesterday, calendar, diary, chart.

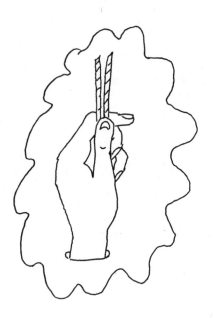

HOW LONG IS A PIECE OF STRING?

Getting children to guess the longest piece of string hidden in your hand is not only a bit of fun—or magic if you do a bit of conjuring—but is also a good introduction to estimating length, learning the vocabulary and starting to measure. Once a piece of string has been picked, you may want to protest that that is not the longest. How can it be put to the test? This is a problem which one of your pupils will probably solve by laying the two pieces side by side. Then everyone can have a go and discuss not only which is longest but which is shortest, too. They will have found that one piece is longer than the other. Once they have got the idea, pupils can play this game amongst themselves.

Other problems can be set in the course of the day, perhaps finding who has the longest pencil or knitted the longest strip of

French knitting or, in a ball game, thrown a ball nearest to the target.

How much longer?
Starting with an easy one, see who can tell you how much longer one row of bricks is than the other. In discussion someone should be able to tell you why—for example because one row is seven bricks long and the other is ten bricks long and is three bricks longer, as can be seen below.

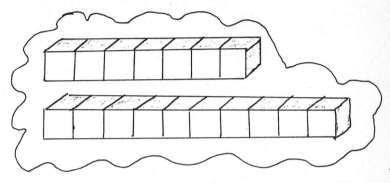

When threading necklaces, the lengths can be compared by counting the number of beads on each lace, so long as the beads are all the same size.

LET'S SEE WHAT ELSE WE CAN MEASURE
Having measured a line of bricks and compared its length with another line, perhaps we could use a row of bricks as a tool for measuring other things as well.

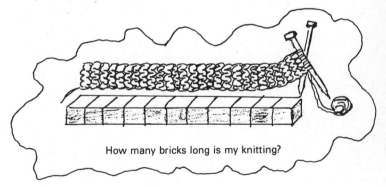

How many bricks long is my knitting?

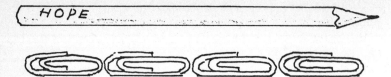

Let's find other things to use for measuring. What about paper clips? How many clips long is my pencil?

It would take too long to measure the bookcase in paper clips. What about hand spans?

How can we measure the rug? What about our own feet placed heel to toe?

Let the class experiment in finding all sorts of different units of measurement and measuring anything that comes to hand.

HEIGHT

Height as well as length can come into this exploratory learning. Making a mark each year on the door jamb may be something that is already done at home. This can encourage the child to grasp the concept of growth and to compare this year's height with last year's. By regular discussion he will learn the meaning of the words 'taller' and 'shorter', etc. If a similar record is kept at school, the heights of different pupils can be compared and the tallest in the class and the shortest noted.

Other growing things can be measured also, except that most plants, for instance, grow very slowly. However, some pot plants grow fairly fast and plotting the growth of an amaryllis can be quite exciting.

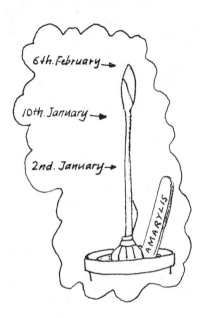

6th. February →

10th. January →

2nd. January →

AMARYLLIS

This period of exploration and discovery of different units of measurement is not wasted. Perhaps two pupils will both be measuring the rug in foot lengths and arrive at different answers. With your help this can lead to the realisation of the need to use a standard measure of length. Now is the time to introduce one of the standard measures. The most obvious one at this point would be a foot. A set of bamboo canes can be cut off so that they each measure exactly a foot in length and the same mat can be measured using these standard 'feet'. Did the two pupils arrive at the same answer this time? They may now appreciate the use of a longer yardstick, and they can mark one off for themselves, using their shorter stick as a measure.

It is best not to introduce more than one unit of length at a time. Once one has been introduced (like the foot) then it should be used as much as possible in practical situations and in woodwork and sewing lessons, for instance, or when moving the furniture around and finding what will fit where.

Old habits die hard and you will notice that the first standard measure I have introduced is a foot. At present measurement in millimetres, centimetres and metres has not completely taken over from yards, feet and inches. Most rulers have both, and material is still often bought by the yard. Our old measures still roughly equate with the human body—feet for distances and hands for height. A rough yard can be measured by stretching out your right arm and turning your head to the left and measuring from the tip of your fingers to the tip of your nose. People still use these rough measures when estimating how much material they have and whether it is enough for a particular purpose. Starting with yards, feet and inches enables children to estimate lengths more easily than starting with metres.

It is a good thing to encourage estimations and to use a standard measure to check the accuracy of your guess.

Estimating

Estimating or guessing lengths, heights and depths should be encouraged. On special occasions a competition with a prize could be staged, for example, 'Guess the length of this pencil and write it down.' The person with the nearest guess gets the pencil. A little subtraction sum could be carried out to find the difference.

Estimations will help in practical situations and educate children to reject a ridiculous answer which may have arisen from incorrect measurement, such as measuring from the wrong end of a tape measure or starting to measure from the figure 1 on a ruler instead of from the 0 at the end.

MAKING YOUR OWN RULER OR MEASURING ROD

The first ruler or measuring rod should only be concerned with one unit of measurement: a start can be made with inches.

Lengths of stiff card one inch wide and twelve inches long are cut out with a Stanley knife. These are accurately measured out in inches, it will save time if the whole sheet of card is marked out first and the strips then cut from it.

Each child should have one strip and should colour in alternate inches very carefully. The first ruler need not be numbered, it can be laid beside the object to be measured and the number of inches counted.

Just as when we were using unconventional measures such as bricks, we had to be sure we did not merely say 'seven', but seven *bricks* long, so now it is important to say seven *inches* long.

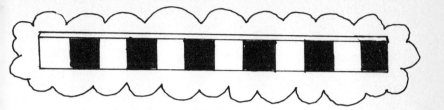

A WORKING TOOL

This first ruler is not a toy but a working tool and should be treated as such. To make it more durable it could be covered in library film—or varnished with polyurethane varnish. Alternatively, if there is an available supply, it can be made of wood instead or cardboard. It should always be kept in a place where it is readily available and not squashed, sucked or bent. Above all, it should be *used*. As Alan Graham remarked in *Help Your Child with Maths*, 'Measuring is not an end in itself but a useful aid to answering a question.'

Perhaps you are into indoor plants. The ruler can be used to measure the size of the pot you will need for potting on, or the size of the saucer. Are you making or buying a necklace and how long do you want it? Is it going to be a long one or a choker? Think how the foot rule can be used here. Perhaps the addition of a piece of string would help in solving this problem.

If you wanted to know the depth of the water in the fish tank, how would you set about it without getting your ruler wet? See what solutions to this problem your pupils or children come up with.

The ruler can also be taken to the woodwork session, or you might simply want to know how long a spoon will be needed to go into the pickle jar.

Practice in measuring is essential, and the child who knows how to use this simple tool to solve real problems will soon be ready for a ruler marked in inches and half and quarter inches.

Do not be in too much of a hurry to move on, for it is only through constantly putting his measuring to use that your pupil will learn to understand and appreciate the principles of using a standard measure. If the emphasis is on the practical he will begin to realise that a foot rule is not an adequate tool with which to solve all his problems. Perhaps at Christmas or for somebody's birthday you could make a cake and then, with some coloured paper, make a fancy frill to go around the cake, after it has been baked and iced. The problem is to get the frill to fit. How can you get a strip of paper the right length? Instead of just providing the answer, give your pupil the opportunity to try and work it out.

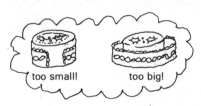

Perhaps you could use some strips of crêpe paper to make paper hats for the party? Here again you may run into trouble!

too big!   too small!

In trying to solve these problems and to make frills and hats that just fit, the pupil is discovering that as well as measuring lengths or widths or heights or depths, we sometimes need to measure the distance *round* an object. If we knew how many inches went round Mary's head, we might be able to find a strip of paper that length and make a crown to fit.

It is a good thing to encourage the pupil to improvise and try to measure with a piece of string or with the paper itself. He will begin to realise that we could do with a different sort of measure which is not hard and straight like a ruler but could be bent around things. What could it be made of? String? A strip of paper? Or a length of tape? It would also save time if this measure was marked out in inches like the ruler. Another thing emerges when we are making the paper crowns: our ruler is not really long enough and we could do with something longer than one foot.

Improvising

Now is the time to raid the junk store and try to improvise a useful measure for such occasions. You could try out strips of paper, lengths of ribbon or tape. Perhaps there is some material left over from shower curtains or kitchen blinds which could be cut into strips. This should be a busy but brainstorming session where ideas are pooled and models are tried out and criticised.

Whatever material is chosen, a decision has to be taken as to how long the measure needs to be. This should also be discussed and the decision may be that it should be at least three times as long as the ruler to stretch round heads (for hats and crowns) or round waists (for belts and cummerbunds).

Each student can get to work using his ruler to mark out inches on the tape. Perhaps colouring in every alternate square will no longer be necessary (it would be difficult and time-consuming with so long a strip). When the tapes are marked out in inches, the pupils should try using them for measuring, for example, round the dustbin!

This brings another problems to light. When measuring small objects with a ruler it was easy to count and remember the number of inches. When measuring round the dustbin it is easy to forget how far it is.

This naturally leads to the idea of numbering the inches on the measuring tape. You may have to experiment before finding the ideal marker for this. If you are using tape or material for your measure, then you could use a Pentel Dyeing Pastel for doing the marking. When the materials are ironed the marks will be permanent.

When finished the tape will look something like this:

If they have been careful and accurate, each pupil will now have another practical and useful tool which they can put to good use. The tape is three times as long as the ruler which was one foot long; perhaps the feet could be marked in a different colour and the pupils could be shown that three feet is called a yard.

This measure should be put to use to find bust measurements, hip measurements, waist measurements, skirt and trouser lengths and possibly sleeve lengths as well. At this point it is important to keep a record of this information either in words or with a diagram.

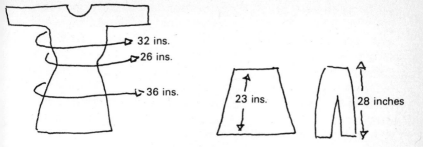

It is useful if these measurements are checked and kept by the pupil in a reference book, for use when buying clothes or patterns to make clothes.

Metrication

So far all the suggestions have been in feet and inches but you may want to introduce centimetres and metres at this stage.

Metrication was introduced into this country in 1970, but has been slow to take over the Imperial or English measure which was used before. Both systems are still usually taught in schools.

Many of us still have difficulty in converting one into the other and this is a rough table which may help:

One metre is about 39 inches
One inch is roughly 2 centimetres
One foot is roughly 30 centimetres
One mile is roughly 1,500 metres

A ruler similar to the foot rule could be marked out in centimetres instead of inches and every alternate centimetre of the thirty coloured in.

A metric tape measure can also be made, one metre long, but it will require more time and patience to make than the tape-measure for one yard, as one hundred squares will have to be marked in very accurately. Much will depend upon the age and ability of the pupils, but the metric measure might well be left to the next stage.

Bought rulers and tape measures

To mark the achievement of those pupils who can be relied upon to make and record accurate measurements, rulers and tape measures can now be bought at the shops. Start with a simple ruler marked out in inches, half inches and quarter inches, if you can get one. Tenths and eighths of an inch can be confusing.

Similarly, with a tape measure, start with a simple one.

Working out and recording problems

At this stage problems of a practical nature can be recorded and solved. Older pupils, for instance, may want to work out how much material they will need to make curtains for their bedroom windows. As we all know to our cost, it is often quite a knotty problem deciding how many widths are needed, adding enough for a hem and the rufflette tape and then measuring the drop. At first pupils may only be capable of helping rather than solving the complete problem. They should be encouraged to help in measuring the window and the width of the material and perhaps trying to 'guesstimate' the amount of material that will be needed. In the woodwork or arts and crafts classes the problems are likely to be easier, while still requiring some calculation.

DISTANCES

In estimating distances it is common practice to estimate yards in strides and feet in heel-to-toe footsteps.

Such estimation gives one a 'feel' for distances travelled. It may be through a game of cricket, in order to find the position of the crease or the distance from one wicket to another, or through playing darts, to position the players fairly. Playground games like 'Grandmother's Footsteps' require all the players to be the same distance from the 'Grandmother', and a set distance from the target is important in a game of marbles. This crude way of measuring distance should be encouraged; the length of the lawn for a race can be measured in this way, and so on. Once more accurate measuring tapes have been acquired, the guess or estimate can be checked by using these.

Nowadays the feel for longer distances is often second hand. By travelling by car or bus we may begin to appreciate mileage.

A mile-long walk will certainly alter this idea of distance. When taking a walk it is important to discuss how far it will be to the park, for instance—half a mile, a quarter of a mile, or what? Young people may get a kick out of recording their walks and finding they can go a little further every time. If they also time themselves, this adds another dimension. I know some young people with severe learning difficulties who have very little idea of distance and expect to be able to get from Land's End to John o' Groats before breakfast. They will benefit from frequent discussion of distances travelled, either every day in the taxi or bus, or on special occasions when an outing is planned.

These practical experiences are of more immediate value then knowing how many yards there are in a mile, or metres in a kilometre.

Vocabulary
Far, near, long, short, broad, narrow, wide, high, low, shallow, deep, length, depth, height, width, distance.

Longer, shorter, smaller, bigger, wider, narrower, deeper, shallower, higher, lower.

Longest, shortest, smallest, biggest, widest, narrowist, deepest, shallowest, lowest.

Measurement, waist measurement, bust measurement, hip measurement, skirt length, trouser length.

Inch, foot, yard, mile, centimetre, metre, kilometre.

Strides, footsteps, hand-spans.

Practical activities are nearly always the first stage in the learning process. They should not therefore be thought of as a waste of time. There is a no point in children doing a very complicated calculation if they don't understand what they are doing. Without understanding the amount of maths that children can learn and the situation in which they can use it are both severely limited.

Merttens, R., *Parent's Guide to Your Child's Maths*

To the above quotation I would add the corollary that you do not need to be unduly concerned if your child can use mathematical concepts in everyday life but cannot solve complicated calculations on paper.

This chapter will be concerned with such practical applications of the concepts of weight, capacity and volume in shopping for supplies, cooking and weight watching, to mention a few. Because in such transactions either weight or volume may be used as a measure, these have been taken together. For example, liquid can be measured in fluid ounces (that is, by weight) or in pints or litres (volume). It is easy to be confused between the two words 'volume' and 'capacity', which are sometimes used interchangeably. However, volume refers to the bulk of an object and capacity refers to how much it will hold.

CAPACITY AND VOLUME

When we are young, it is a case of seeing is believing: if something *looks* longer or fatter than something else then, for a small child, it *is* longer or fatter. Even as we grow older we tend to believe the evidence of our own eyes unless we are subsequently proved wrong. However, appearances can be deceptive. Try this experiment. Below are two straight lines. Can you tell if one is longer than the other? Which one is longer? Now measure the two lines and see if you were right.

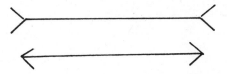

Perhaps you have met this phenomenon before, in which case you will not have been taken in. This goes to show the importance of previous experience if we are not to be deceived.

It is much harder to estimate volume than it is to estimate length. Given two different-shaped wine glasses, can you be sure that you have poured the same amount into each? A child will probably choose the one that looks the most.

Experimenting with volume
Ensure that your child is actively involved in experimentation with volume both at home and in school. There will be plenty of opportunities, but only with your guidance is he likely to make the most of them.

FULL AND EMPTY
These terms are often used loosely but it is important that a child grasps their exact meaning. The orange juice bottle will be full when it comes from the shop, but when some of the juice has been drunk it is no longer full. When playing on the beach or in the sandpit, show him how he can fill a bucket completely, using the spade to remove excessive sand and to straighten out the top, and then empty it to make a sand castle. Small children love to fill a bucket with water and then empty it out. Perhaps the words full and empty could be used when a pupil is helping to water the pot plants or to give round the milk.

COMPARING VOLUMES
It may take a child a long time before he is convinced that there is the same amount of coke in the two containers overleaf.

Who has the most coke?

This will only come with direct experience of pouring liquid from one to the other and back again. Liquid is the first thing that comes to mind in these experiments but it has its drawbacks, the main one being that some of it will probably get spilt, and this will make the experiment less convincing. Another drawback in using liquid for more accurate experiments is that you cannot fill a container completely: if you do, the liquid is liable to spill over. Children do need to experience filling containers up to the brim and checking the level with something like a palette knife. Many substances can be used instead of liquid. Dry silver sand which will pour almost as well and can be brushed up if it spills. Sawdust is another possibility and rice, peas, beans or lentils can be used from the kitchen cupboard. It is a pity to waste food, so these should be measured out when they are needed or kept very clean and tipped back again.

GUESS HOW MANY
Use some small containers like cream or yoghurt cartons. See how many yoghurt cartons of water will go into the teapot after first hazarding a guess. Or try tipping cartons of washing powder into a container and seeing how many it will hold.

These skills can be a step towards independent living. The containers need to be varied as much as possible and, as well as cups and mugs and cartons, the children should practise measuring out spoonfuls into a container. Even before any mention has been made of standard measures of capacity (pints, quarts, litres), these readily available measures can be put to use.

COOKERY

Sometimes children are not allowed to help in the kitchen until they are fully capable. I think that is a mistake, as even a young child can be taught essential safety rules and, once he has learnt to measure out cupfuls, cartonfuls and spoonfuls, he can be a real help in preparing ingredients even if he cannot yet accomplish the whole cooking process.

With a group of children there may be some who can follow a recipe and cook almost independently, while others are only at the stage of measuring out the flour or butter. This does not matter: they can all be part of the team and help to taste the results!

Many suitable recipes can be found in *Cookery for Handicapped People* by James Hargreaves. No weighing is required to follow these recipes which are shown in pictures stage by stage.

You may find some old recipe books helpful. This fudge recipe was a great favourite at one village school and selling the fudge brought in school funds.

FUDGE

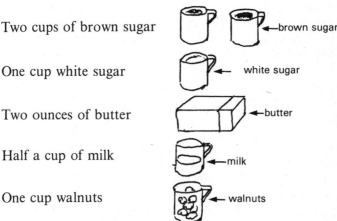

Two cups of brown sugar   ←brown sugar

One cup white sugar   ← white sugar

Two ounces of butter   ←butter

Half a cup of milk   ←milk

One cup walnuts   ← walnuts

Boil for three to five minutes. Remove from heat.

Warning. With inexperienced cooks this fudge making must be well supervised as boiling sugar can cause a nasty burn. If the adult has to do this part, the children can do the rest and mark out the fudge in squares, so learning something about area, too!

Using single units of measurement

As in the measurement of length, single units of measurement should be introduced first, for example a cup, a yoghurt pot or a spoon. The unit of measurement does not have to be a standard unit. For instance, concentrated fruit juice may need to be diluted with one part of juice to six parts of water, and any suitable unit can be used to measure the proportions of juice to water. This is a practical exercise to accustom children to the idea of measurement of volume, and they will need to keep a tally on the number of cupfuls which have gone in. Similarly, washing powder is often measured with a measuring cup. In the potting shed the potting compost can be measured out with so many parts of sand and so many of peat and so on.

Spoons are often used to measure sugar.

Practice in measuring out quantities with different units of measurement will be needed before standard measures are introduced.

Standard measures

Despite the introduction of metric measures, British Imperial measures are still in general use and involve much smaller numbers than the metric system. I suggest that a start should be made with one pint, a measure with which the pupils will already be familiar. For measuring larger quantities two pints or a quart and then a gallon can be introduced.

You will need
A milk bottle
A clear carton (individual desserts are sold in these at the supermarket)
A permanent projector pen
A bucket
A measuring jug
A funnel

To prepare
Measure out a quarter of a pint of water, pour this into the clear carton and mark the level of the water with the overhead projector pen. This is then used as a unit of measure.

The pupils can then make their own measure by pouring first a quarter of a pint into a milk bottle and marking the level of the water and then filling their carton again and adding another quarter of a pint, and so on. They will have a measuring bottle in pints, three-quarter pints, half pints and quarter pints. These should be marked on the bottle as shown below. When they are familiar with using this simplified measure they can find the Imperial measure on their measuring jug and use that.

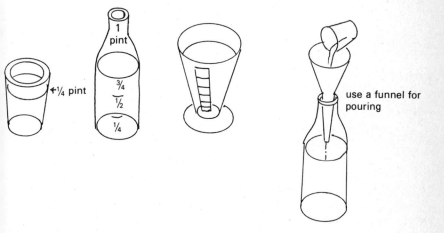

Using their calibrated bottle, pupils can now measure out liquids in the cookery lesson or when they are making drinks. They can also use the pint bottle as a unitary measure to measure out quarts and gallons in making up mixtures for the garden, for instance.

The standard measuring jug usually includes many different measures, such as for flour, sugar, rice, etc., which are useful in the cookery lesson. These are somewhat easier to use than scales but do not in themselves lead to an understanding of comparative weights.

Vocabulary
Full, empty, half full, a quarter full, three quarters full, pint, quart, gallon, liquid, level.

WEIGHTS

In order to understand what is meant by weight, a child needs to gain personal experience of objects and substances which are light or heavy to carry. You will need carrier bags for this and a series of substances of differing weight but similar size—cartons of sugar, boxes of feathers or kapok, lead weights, etc.

Let the children first guess whether a substance is light or heavy to carry. Other objects, such as golf balls and lightweight ping pong balls, can be held in the hand and compared.

Make plenty of opportunities during the day for comparing the weight of different things.

You can move on when your pupils are reasonably familiar with the idea that the weight of an object is not directly related to its size or bulk.

Using a balance

Different weights can now be compared with the use of a balance. The seesaw in the playground is one kind of balance with which the children will be familiar, and with your help and guidance they will learn about different weights by experimenting with classmates on the seesaw. They can guess which child is the heavier of the two and so learn some of the language of weighing also.

In the classroom some balancing scales should be provided. A ruler could be used to improvise these, but you will also need to buy a reliable set of scales. Do not introduce standard weights until the children have had an opportunity to experiment with balancing many different objects on the two pans. Guessing which is going to be the heavier should be encouraged here also. Some small but heavy objects should be contrasted with larger, lighter objects.

The next step is to choose some objects which all weigh the same. Two pence pieces are a handy measure to choose. Again a number of small objects are assembled and the children take turns to guess how many two pence pieces will balance with each. Alternatively, they could have a fixed number of coins on one pan and choose something to balance that number. The teacher or parent can help by guiding the conversation: 'My chocolate weighs more than ten coins.' 'My pen is lighter.' 'These two just balance, they weigh the same.'

Using standard weights

It is easiest to begin with British Imperial weights. Balances that are sensitive enough to weigh grams are not suitable for beginners to use. Ounce weights make a good initial standard measure and eight of these should be provided at first. At this stage there is no need to refer to pounds, but many objects should be weighed in ounces. Sweets can be weighed out in the school shop or ingredients in the cookery lesson. When the children can measure goods correctly and easily up to eight ounces, some more ounce weights could be introduced until they have a maximum of sixteen ounces. Weighing with these one ounce weights needs to be thoroughly practised before a one pound weight is produced. Children should have the opportunity to handle this weight and to guess how many ounces it might weigh before checking by putting it on one end of the balance and putting one ounce weights on the other. When they have discovered that the bigger weight weighs sixteen ounces they can also be told that it is called a pound. Heavier objects can now be weighed and single ounces added to the pound weight. Using the the sixteen one ounce weights, the children can divide them into two sets (halve them) and discover that half of a pound is eight ounces. They should then be given a half pound weight with which to check their results and should divide their sets again to come to a quarter pound weight. Most of their practical weighing of goods and purchases, and of ingredients for cookery, will only need these weights.

Practice with household ingredients such as rice, lentils, beans, peas and small potatoes should be continued for as long as possible before introducing the more conventional scales. Suitable scales with both English and metric calibration can be bought from Philip and Tacey and are called Waymaster Add-and-weigh.

Bodyweight

In these days of weight watching, a knowledge of measurement of bodyweight is of practical importance. Most bathroom scales are calibrated in both standard measures (stones and pounds and kilograms). Seize any opportunity to let your child experience the weight of a stone, perhaps by trying to lift a stone of potatoes. It is not very practical to try balancing fourteen pounds against a stone, and the fact that fourteen pounds weigh a stone may have to be taken on trust. Let the pupils weigh themselves and keep a record of their own weight. A class record can also be kept. Any pupil who is on a diet and trying to lose weight should be weighed at regular intervals and the weight recorded.

Perhaps the pupils could visit the school store and see potatoes and heavy goods being weighed.

Formal work

Formal exercises in adding, subtracting and dividing weights and measures are of no great practical value and do not usually lead to increased understanding. However, some calculations are of ongoing importance. Recipes are often written with the amount of ingredients for four people and it is useful to be able to calculate amounts for a different number of people, perhaps eight or six or two. I think that written sums are largely unnecessary for this kind of calculation, but pupils may need some extra help in solving the problem.

Structured material such as that used in the addition and subtraction, multiplication and division of tens and units can be brought into play (see Chapters 12 and 13). If sticks are used and the problem is one of weight, each stick can represent one ounce and bundles of sixteen sticks can represent sixteen ounces or one pound.

Vocabulary
Heavy, light, heavier, lighter, heaviest, lightest, balance, weight, overweight, underweight, weight watching, scales, weights, ounces, pounds, stones.

The activity and language level of the ALPS sequence
From a very early age children play with toys which give them hands-on experience of handling a variety of different geometrical shapes and discovering some of their properties.

When they are playing with bricks (described in Chapter 2) they are handling cubes, cuboids and cylinders and finding how they fit together to construct towers and cars and houses.

Their first posting box will have at least four geometrical shapes made to fit into the holes in the lid (cubes, cuboids, cylinders and pyramids) and later posting boxing will have many more.

From the earliest age they will also be familiar with a ball (sphere).

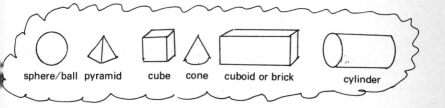

sphere/ball pyramid   cube   cone   cuboid or brick   cylinder

The parent's contribution to these games is to introduce the language which describes these shapes correctly and also draw the child's attention to some of the properties of both solid and two-dimensional shapes. As the child grows older and is preparing himself for school life, the language used should be more exact, for both solid and two-dimensional shapes.

Some of the relevant terms will be listed here, and also further games and activities which will focus the child's attention on the relevant dimensions.

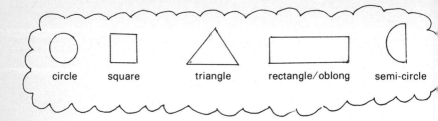

circle   square   triangle   rectangle/oblong   semi-circle

Language
Ball (sphere), cube, cylinder, pyramid, cuboid.
Round (circle), square, oblong (rectangle), triangle, egg-shape (oval).
Sides (faces), edges, corners, flat, curved, shape, size.

Games and activities

POSTING BOXES
Guess the hole: take the pieces out of a posting box (use only four basic shapes at first). Lay out one set on a table and put the others in a bag or pillowcase. The game is to put your hand in the bag and, without looking, pick out a shape and feel it. Keep it in your hand without looking and point to the shape on the table which you think is the same. Check by taking your shape out of the bag. Was it the same? If not, discuss how it was different. When playing this game and taking turns to guess, the correct names should be used for the shapes as they are identified.

Another version of the game is to ask children in turn to put their hand in the bag and, without looking, find a 'cube' or a 'sphere' or a 'cuboid'. If they are not sure what you mean, point to the shape on the table until they get used to the proper names.

SORTING BY SHAPE
The idea of sorting objects by different attributes is already familiar to the children and they have sorted objects by colour, use and texture, perhaps. They now have to understand that objects can be quite different in colour, size, use or texture and still be the same basic *shape*.

You will need
The four basic shapes from the posting box or box of bricks. A collection of items in these four shapes that vary in size, colour and use, for example:

Cylinders: jars, kitchen rolls, tins, batteries, cotton reels, corks.

Cubes: cubes of sugar, Oxo cubes, boxes, dice.

Cuboids: shoe boxes, matchboxes, soap cartons, tablets of soap.

Spheres: ping pong balls, marbles, tennis balls, balls of wool.

Start a sorting game with just two shapes which are very different, such as cylinders and cuboids. Put one of each basic shape on a sheet of paper or in a container and let your pupil sort out the others which are the same shape, for example, all the cuboids here and all the cylinders there. When he can do this, add a third shape and then a fourth.

OUT OF DOORS
When out for a drive or going for walk, ask who can see anything which is shaped like a cylinder. Without practice most people find it quite hard to isolate shapes from a crowded landscape and you may have to start the ball rolling. Here are some cylinders you might see round about: pillar boxes, bollards, tree trunks, telegraph poles.

Another day be on the lookout for a different shape, a cuboid, perhaps. You can pay the same shapes game around the house where you will find cylindrical jars and lampshades and plant pots and cuboid radios, books, and boxes and sugar lump cubes and Oxo cubes.

TWO-DIMENSIONAL SHAPES FROM SOLIDS
Make a collection of small objects of different shapes. A beginning can be made with corks (cylinders), erasers of different sizes (cuboids), wooden cubes and small rubber or ping pong balls.

Experiment with these to find, with your pupils, which will stand on a flat surface without rolling. Discuss the reason why some will stand whichever way up they are put (cubes and cuboids), some have to be put the right way up or they will roll (cylinders) and some will not stand firm whichever way up they are put (spheres). The words 'flat', 'surface', 'face', 'edges', 'corners' and 'curves' can be introduced in this discussion.

The next step is for your pupils to choose the solids which will stand firm on a flat surface, that is, those with two or more flat faces. They can then experiment with making prints from these flat faces, either with a printing ink pad or some poster paint mixed with paste.

The corks and erasers should make good, clear prints but you may have to glue a piece of material or felt on the cube to get a clear print. After the pupils have had plenty of opportunity to experiment and to make a variety of patterns with their prints, it is time to talk about their shape, and to find all the rectangles (oblongs), squares, circles and triangles. Talk about the edges, the shapes with straight edges and those with curved edges.

Some games to play
The following games will consolidate what has been learnt and give further practice in shape recognition and naming.

A RACE GAME
On a sheet of stiff card draw out a board as shown opposite. Prints for the various shapes can be made from potato cuts. Either make a spinner with shapes in the segments or buy some blank dice from E. J. Arnold and print different shapes on each face. Different-coloured counters for each player are also needed.

This is a simplified version of a game called 'Shaping Up', marketed by Philip and Tacey Ltd, which although excellent, is not quite suitable as part of a first introduction to shape since it involves both colour and shape recognition. In the version here, each player throws a dice in turn and moves his counter to the first square on the track with that shape.

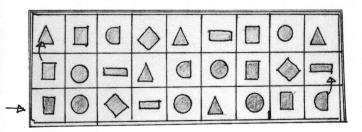

PAIRS

Blank playing cards can be purchased from a number of educational suppliers (Waddingtons, or E. J. Arnold). These are a good investment as children like playing with them and games can be made to match their level of development.

For 'Pairs', duplicate sets of cards are prepared with regular shapes printed on the face. As with other games of pairs described in this book, the cards are scattered face down on the table and in turn each player turns up two cards without altering their position on the table. If the two cards match, the player has to name the shape and can take the two cards. If they do not match he has to turn them over just where they were before. When all the cards have been claimed the player with the most pairs wins. The players have to remember where the different shapes are and this not only helps their memory and concentration but also keeps their eye in for shape.

BINGO

A game of bingo can be made with shapes instead of numbers, and also a set of shape dominoes. In both these games the players will learn most if they name the shapes when they claim them or match them.

DRAWING ROUND SHAPES

Pupils can collect a number of objects such as tins, cotton reels, boxes of different sizes, large dice, etc., and practise drawing round them and then colouring them in. If they have a new page for each shape, they will be practising their sorting skills since each shape will have several examples which differ in size.

MAKING NETS

Encourage your pupils to draw round the edges of the different faces of regular solids. This will give them some understanding of the number and shape of the faces that go to make up a solid. Encourage them to collect boxes of different sizes and cylindrical objects. The pupils who become quite adept at this can go on to making 'nets' for model making. If they are folded exactly on the lines, they can be stuck together to make cardboard models. Sellotape can be used to fasten the edges together. Pupils will probably need your help initially and if the solid object is kept inside the model until the last face is ready to be stuck down, this will make the task much easier.

SOME NETS YOU CAN MAKE

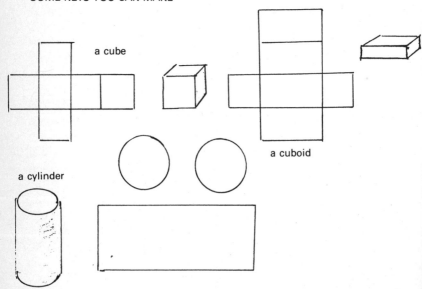

a cube

a cuboid

a cylinder

CALCULATING AREA AND VOLUME

Each pupil is given a set number of cubes and tries out how many different shapes he can build with them. They should be compared and discussed: 'Those two towers have the same number of cubes but one is higher than the other which is longer.'

It can be pointed out that towers with the same number of cubes have the same volume. Let them tell you the volume of each tower—for example, twelve cubes, ten cubes or twenty-four cubes.

Let the pupils experiment with making shapes with many different numbers of cubes and tell you the volume of each in cubes: 'The volume of this train is twenty-four cubes,' for instance.

Building cubes are often roughly an inch wide and pupils should now begin to measure them with a ruler. Then it can be explained that instead of giving the volume in 'cubes' which could be any size, the volume should be expressed in 'cubic inches'.

SUGAR CUBES

There are some small sugar cubes on the market which are one cubic centimetre. These can be measured and then counted and put back in the box layer by layer. The number of rows in each layer is counted and the number of cubes in each row. Multiplying the number of rows by the number of cubes in each row tells you the number of cubes in one layer. The number of layers in the box is then counted and multiplied by the number of cubes in each layer to give the volume of sugar cubes in cubic centimetres.

Capacity

Now is the time to look at a collection of cubes, cuboids and cylinders and discover that some are solid shapes and others are hollow. Each pupil should be given a collection to sort out into solid or hollow shapes. The hollow shapes should include boxes with lids that can be opened. They then focus on the idea that hollow objects will *hold* other things. Some, like a cylindrical vase, will hold water. Others, like the sugar lump box, will hold cubes. Some boxes hold very few cubes and others hold a lot. Similarly, some vases or jugs hold very little and some hold a lot of water or milk. The amount they hold is called their *capacity*. The example of the box for cubes of sugar can again be used. The number of cubic centimetres it will hold is its cubic capacity. For pupils who cannot yet deal with such large numbers, a box of Oxo cubes can be used to demonstrate.

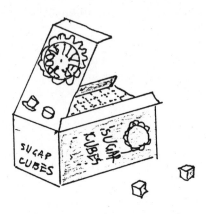

A GAME TO PLAY

You will need to make a cardboard box for each pupil to hold an exact number of wooden cubes (see p. 162 for making nets for cuboid shapes), and provide a dice or spinner and sufficient wooden cubes to fill the boxes.

To play

Each player in turn throws the dice and counts out that number of cubes and arranges them in his box. The winner is the one to fill his box first with the exact number of cubes. They should then be ready to tell you the cubic capacity of the box. I suggest that boxes should not be made too large and that one with a capacity of 30 cubes (three rows of ten) would be about right and also easy to calculate.

Language

Solid, hollow, layers, rows, length, breadth, width, height, Cube, cubic, capacity, volume, number it will hold.

AREA

An introduction has already been made to two-dimensional shapes which have been used to print patterns or made by drawing round the faces of solid objects. The focus will now be on squares, as this is the unit of measurement for areas.

You will need a good supply of squared paper or exercise books. Those marked out in centimetre squares are a good size to choose. You will also need coloured pencils for accurate colouring.

Pupils should now be encouraged to colour in a lot of different-sized squares or rectangles (oblongs) on their squared paper and then count how many squares go to make up each shape. The number of squares can be printed under each shape. It can be pointed out that the number of squares in a shape is called the *area*. They can then be encouraged to be more creative and to make patterns using different colours on their squared paper, and when they have finished their patterns to count the number of squares for each pattern. They can be shown the quick way of finding the number of squares by counting one row of squares and then counting how many rows they have used. The number of squares will be the number in a row times the number of rows.

The next step is to measure one of the squares (one centimetre) and to record the area in square centimetres.

A COLOURING GAME

You will need
A dice (or two) for each pupil, squared paper and coloured pencils.

To play
Throw the dice and colour in an area of that size.

Larger areas

When furnishing a room and buying carpets, vinolay or mats and making curtains we need to calculate larger areas.

Floors are often tiled in squares and counting or calculating the number of squares on the floor makes a good introduction. The exact size of the tiles is not important at first and the area can be described in square tiles. Many floor tiles are one square metre and so the area can be exactly measured in square metres.

At home children can help to work out how big a bathmat will be needed in the bathroom, or a rug for their bedroom, by measuring the length and breadth of the floor space and multiplying the length times the breadth.

KNITTING BLANKETS
A worthwhile project for a school or club would be to knit squares for a blanket for the Third World. The size of the squares has to be decided (they are more accurate if knitted from corner to corner) and then the size of the finished blanket. In this way you will know how many squares will be needed and can allocate a number for each knitter. The area of the blanket does not need to be calculated in feet or inches or centimetres at this stage, but in squares. One sample square should be knitted first and used as a measure.

EMBROIDERY AND RUGMAKING
Patterns for embroidery (cross stitch) and rugmaking can be drawn out on squared paper after the area of the finished article has been decided.

MAKING PLANS
How about measuring the playground or the lawn at home in strides, and then calculating the area by multiplying the length times the breadth. This is a harder task as there are no squares marked out to help you. A plan to scale of the playground or the lawn should then be drawn out on the squared paper. This can lead on to making plans of the class-room or eventually the whole school. At this stage it is best to deal only with single measurements of length and breadth—strides or foot-steps (heel to toe) or feet—as otherwise you are introducing an added complication and very complicated calculations.

Language
Area, square inches, square feet, square centimetres, length, breadth, plans, to scale, surface, foot, yard, metre.

JANE'S PLAN OF HER BEDROOM

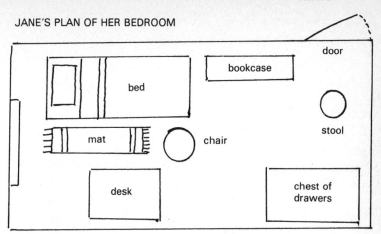

More formal work

With a simple centimetre rule let the children measure the tops of things around the room, for example, radios, pencil boxes, matchboxes, tins. When they have measured the longest side and the width they can record their measurement in a sum: 16 centimetres × 5 = 80 square centimetres. If necessary they can check the answer by using their squared paper, but later they should not need it.

The area of irregular shapes

Let the children experiment with irregular shapes by laying leaves, circles and triangles onto their squared paper and seeing how many squares are covered. This will be the area of the shape in square centimetres.

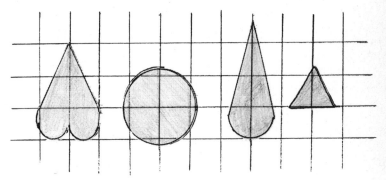

TESSELATION

Children should experience that it is not only squares which can exactly cover an area. They can experiment in making patterns with other shapes, perhaps using a fifty pence piece to start with and then printing different shapes with a potato cut, for instance.

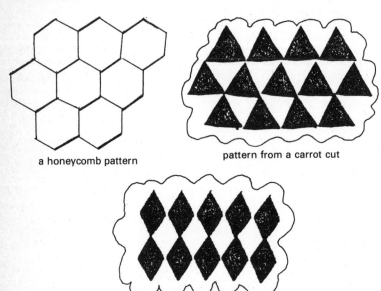

a honeycomb pattern

pattern from a carrot cut

a diamond shaped carrot cut

As any mother will tell you, young children have little idea of the value of money and will often set their hearts on having something very expensive which takes their fancy in the shops. This is also true of young people who have severe learning difficulties, and who in their teens may still have very little idea of the value of money.

This is partly due to the complexity of money values, which depend upon many economic factors and also upon the amount people are willing to pay (for instance for paintings by Turner). Also the size of an object gives no hint of its value. Parents usually ensure that their children gradually begin to understand the value of money by giving them a regular amount of pocket money, which sometimes has to be earned by doing little jobs around the house. In a survey of teenagers with severe learning difficulties we found, by talking to the parents, that they were seldom given regular amounts of pocket money. If they wanted something, like a record, their parents put the correct amount of money in their hands which they then gave to the shop assistant. These teenagers, not surprisingly, had very little idea of the value of money.

Exchange

Historically, before monetary systems came into use, goods were bartered or exchanged. Perhaps children need to go through the stage of bartering actual goods before they can understand the use of money. Most children do, in fact, swap their possessions with their friends at some time in their lives Heated discussions of relative worth often take place.

Primitive tribes gradually found that bartering of goods in this way was often cumbersome and began to use a system of tokens, such as cowrie shells, as a means of exchange. The use of some such token economy can give children the idea of using tokens as a rate of exchange. They will gain a better idea of relative values if they have to do something in order to earn these tokens. They could be earned by carrying out routine tasks or even earned for good behaviour. The next step would be to exchange these tokens for a variety of desirable goodies. Some would be exchanged for a few tokens and some for many more, according to an agreed tariff.

Soon a unitary coin can be substituted for the tokens. A one penny piece is probably the best to start with. When enough of these have been earned they can be exchanged for goodies in shops as well as at home or school.

A small child, or an older child with learning difficulties, will need time to experience even this simple economy, since it means that satisfaction is delayed and not immediate. Two stages of exchange now have to be accomplished before final satisfaction is reached: the tokens or pennies must be earned and then exchanged for the appropriate goodies. Parents or teachers will have to monitor the system to ensure that the child does get what he wants without intolerable delay.

CHANGING YOUR MONEY

The child who has collected a heap of pennies before using them to buy what he wants will begin to realise that handfuls of pennies are rather cumbersome when one is out shopping.

Now is the time to introduce the idea of changing numbers of pennies for one single coin (a ten pence piece).

Games to play at this stage will be found on pp. 72 and 98 and will help a child to understand the relative values of these two coins.

COIN RECOGNITION

So far only ten pence and one penny coins have been used. The next coin to be introduced is the two pence piece. Make sure that all your pupils can match and sort out these three coins. This can be a natural thing to do if they are given a pile of coins and three containers. They will also become accustomed to the names (and values) of these three coins if they do enough sorting and talk about it. Handy coin rubber stamps (Philip and Tacey Ltd.) can be used to help coin recognition. Here is a game to play. You will need a spinner, coin cards and coins.

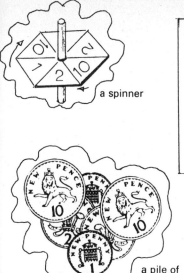

a spinner

a coin card for each pupil

a pile of
coins

To play

Each player spins the top in turn and takes the appropriate coin
out of the kitty and covers the coin on his card. The player to
complete his card first is the winner. This game is more fun for
a small group to play, but some pupils might like to play on
their own and see how quickly they can complete their
card.

When these three coins are recognised without hesitation,
a five pence coin can be added to the game.

Recognition of coins should go hand in hand with recognising
their value.

HOW CAN I MAKE TEN PENCE?

Pupils can now be helped to select some coins which exactly
add up to ten pence. If this is being done with a group of pupils,
they can see that they have not all selected the same coins. See if
anyone can suggest other ways of making ten pence. They
might then be allowed to use the rubber stamps to record their
work in their own books as follows:

ANOTHER GAME TO PLAY—'Add up to ten'
Collect one, two and five pence coins for the kitty.

Select the aces, twos and fives cards from a pack of playing cards.

The playing cards are placed in a pack face down. Each player in turn takes the top card off the pack and selects a coin of that denomination from the kitty and places his card at the bottom of the pack. The first player to collect coins which add up to ten pence is the winner. If they pick a card which makes their total more than ten pence they miss a turn and put that card back.

Introducing fifty pence
When a new coin is introduced it is important that the pupils should be able to match and sort all the coins they have handled so far. They can now play the coin recognition game in a new version. Their coin cards should now include one, two, five, ten and fifty pence coins and these should also be in the kitty (plastic coins *can* be used, but it is much better to use real ones if the budget will stretch that far).

The card game 'Add up to ten' can now be played and the

tens cards can be added to the pack collected. The game is to collect coins which exactly add up to fifty pence in order to win.

HOW MANY WAYS TO MAKE FIFTY PENCE?
Starting off with five ten pence pieces, see if your pupils can think of other combinations of coins which will add up to fifty pence.

Let them use the rubber stamps to record their findings in their books.

The one pound coin
As with the other coins, make sure all the children can match, sort, recognise and name this coin.

A new version of the coin recognition game can now be played with one, two, five and ten pence coins stamped on each pupil's card.

A new spinner has to be used with these numbers on as well.

The card game 'Add up to ten' can be played with the one, two, five and ten denomination playing cards. If you have a set of blank playing cards you could add one for fifty.

This time the first player to win a hundred pence (one pound) is the winner.

Money changing games
Games for familiarising the children with changing one penny coins for ten pence pieces have already been described on pp. 72 and 98. The pupils will also have experimented with collections of coins which together make either ten pence or 50 pence. However, because there are many different coins to take into account, they will still need more practice with larger amounts of real money. Having checked the 'dinner money' or money for the holiday yourself, the pupils could be brought in a few at a time to double check.

First, they should be shown how to sort out the different coins, with all the one penny coins first, then the two pence coins, the five pence coins, ten pence coins, fifty pence coins and finally one pound coins.

Starting with the one penny coins they should then put them into piles of ten; similarly with the two pence and five pence coins (if your pupil is not yet familiar with numbers beyond a hundred, the coins of higher denominations should be left until later. The pupils should then count how many complete piles of ten pence they have lined up and count this up in tens, and then how many more pence they have over, for example, ten, twenty, thirty, forty, and six is forty-six pence. If they find the spare coppers add up to another ten, this should be changed into a ten piece piece and counted on. The total can then be recorded with the number of tens on the left and the number of pence left over on the right.

WHAT IS IT WORTH?

Only through experience with shopping do we form a realistic idea of the current prices of goods. Because your child is too young to do the shopping or is unable to cope with it independently, is not a good reason for leaving him out. Certainly, from a very early age he will have to accompany us when we go shopping. I think that gradually he should be given graded amounts of responsibility. A supermarket might be a good place to begin. You could collect some wrappers from groceries which are often on your shopping list, or buy some sets of 'Let's Go Shopping' gummed stamps from Philip and Tacey. Stick a picture or a wrapper on a postcard and give it to your young 'helper'. It is his responsibility to find goods (say, a tin of tomato soup) on the shelves and, if it is in reaching distance, bring it and put in in your trolley. If it cannot be reached easily he will tell you where it is and get you to hand it down. This should not be a 'once off' occurrence but should become part of the shopping routine, with different single items to be bought on different days.

By the time he is able to count out coins in his purse to the value of fifty pence, he can be given his own 'housekeeping purse' and be responsible for paying for the one item at the check-out. If he makes a note of the price at the side of his picture shopping list, all the better. Gradually more items which are his responsibility can be added to the shopping list.

This is an area where home and school can collaborate and pupils can gradually assume responsibility for buying the ingredients for their cookery lessons. Do not wait for your child to be able to read before giving him this experience. Picture lists work quite well, or any label or trade mark to remind him what to buy. Perhaps a small group of pupils might go shopping together and share the responsibility. A 'reader' amongst them could be responsible for checking out the goods. This responsible shopping, which is introducing your pupil to the prices of groceries and other foods in the shops, will be interspersed with more light-hearted sorties to the school shop or sweet shop to spend pocket money. Your knowledge of each pupil's capabilities will enable you to programme what he is asked to do and monitor the results.

The classroom shop
From infancy children today gain experience of buying and selling in the classroom shop. Picture lists of items to be sold, with their prices, are often hung on the wall behind the shop.

In the nursery class it does not matter if the prices are somewhat fanciful, with jars of jam going for six pence, but as the child grows older it is important to get the prices right. Otherwise it is going to be difficult for him to understand the value of money.

Keeping accounts
Some people regularly keep accurate accounts of every penny they have spent, while others are far more casual about money. Children should not be made to account for every penny, if this is not what their parents and teachers have to do. However, it is important to be able to reckon up when need be, especially when you are responsible for other people's money.

When pupils are able to able to record tens and units in columns and add them up with carrying, they will be able to tot up what they have spent at the shops. At first they may need an abacus, or other kinds of structured apparatus to help them get the sum right. They could perhaps then be shown how to check their answers using a pocket calculator.

Budgeting
The first step towards budgeting is thinking ahead. Children sometimes tend towards being impulsive buyers and, if we are truthful, it is not only children who are like this.

As the children become more responsible for doing their own shopping or part of your shopping, it is good to discuss beforehand how much money there is in the kitty and what needs to be bought. This can be done at the same time as making out a list for yourself and one for your child or pupil.

If your child has a set amount of pocket money each week it is a good idea to make him responsible for buying some essential items out of it. As he grows older his responsibilities in this way can be gradually increased and may include bus fares or toothpaste, etc. Show him how to plan his spending, taking these commitments into account.

Banking
The first bank is probably a piggy bank, but when the child is given a savings account he should be told how it works.

Checklists

USE OF CHECKLISTS

The aim of this book is to develop an understanding of numerical concepts through active experience, talking about that experience and using pictures and patterns to record experiences, and finally using numerical symbols to record.

There is no short cut to understanding and the checklists have been put at the end of the book so that they will not be used as teaching objectives but to record the level reached through the activities described in these pages.

A parent or teacher who has actively participated in these activities will know when each milestone has been reached and will record the date of that developmental stage on the checklist.

This will provide an *aide memoire* and also a means by which knowledge can be handed on from class to class, or from teacher to teacher, or from school to home.

If a pupil is unable to complete the checklist at the end of a section, he needs more practice. Increase the amount of practical experience on that topic and devise a varied menu of games to play so that understanding arises out of familiarity.

If you are teaching children with severe learning difficulties, do not expect them to be up to understanding all the sections, For practical purposes this is not essential, and if they have not understood what they are doing they are unlikely to be able to put rote learning to any further use.

SECTION ONE CHECKLIST

	yes	no	date
Matching			
Can match identical objects or pictures			
Can match things that go together, e.g. cups and saucers, tins and lids, straws and milk bottles			
Can match shapes, e.g. squares, circles, triangles			
Can match colours			
Can match pictures or objects which are not identical, e.g. pictures of different houses, pencils, etc.			
Sorting Can sort out two groups of dissimilar objects, e.g. bricks and counters			
Can sort out two groups of similar objects, e.g. buttons and counters			
Can sort out objects according to colour, e.g. red and green			
Can sort out objects according to shape, e.g. round and square			
Can sort objects by two attributes, e.g. shape and colour			
Can classify objects by use, e.g. those we eat			
Can classify and sort objects by function. e.g. clothes, food, furniture, tools			

	yes	no	date
Ordering Can copy a pattern of beads, e.g. —◯△◯△◯△◯△◯△—			
Can continue a pattern started by the teacher, e.g. □×□×□×......			
Can remember the order of daily events, e.g. meals			
Can put rings in order on a stack or stacking beakers			
Conservation Can match up playing cards by the pattern of pips, i.e. up to five			
Can match patterns of pips presented differently, e.g. or			
Realises that a number of objects which have been counted stay the same when spread out			
One-to-one correspondence Can button up a row of buttons without leaving any buttonholes out, or place eggs in egg cups without mistakes.			

Rote counting

a   Ask the pupil to start counting and credit him with the highest number he reaches without mistakes.

b   While the pupil is counting, stop him briefly and ask him to count on. Credit him with the highest number he can count on from correctly.

c   Start the pupil counting forward, 1, 2, 3. Then ask him to count them back. Credit him with the highest number counted correctly in reverse. Make sure he knows what you want by giving some examples.

level reached	1	2	3	4	5	6	7	8	9	10		
a. forward												
b. backward												
c. count on												

If the pupil can count further than 10, credit him with the highest number reached in the blank boxes provided.

Counting out
d   Starting with a small group, ask the pupil how many boys, etc., there are. Credit the highest number he counts correctly with no help from you.
e   Start with a small group of bottles or shoes and get the pupil to count them. Gradually increase the number until you reach his ceiling.
f   Give the pupil beads or other small objects in a box, and ask him to count out a number and put the objects into another box (credit the highest number correctly counted).
g   Ask the pupil to count the spots on a large dice.
h   Using a dice, counter and chequered cloth or board see if the pupil can throw the dice and move the counter forward correctly.

level reached	1	2	3	4	5	6	7	8	9	10		
d. Counts out people												
e. Counts out objects (large—e.g. shoes)												
f. Counts out objects (small—e.g. beads)												
g. Counts out spots on dice												
h. Can move counter correctly to spots on dice												

SECTION TWO CHECKLIST

Ordinal numbers	yes	no	date
Knows who is *first* in a line-up			
Knows who is *last* in a line-up			
Can line up objects in a row and point to the first and last			

	1st	2nd	3rd	4th	5th	6th	7th	8th	9th	10th
In an unnumbered row can point to:										
In an unnumbered row can name:										
In a numbered row can name without counting										

Numerals	1	2	3	4	5	6	7	8	9	10
Can name when in right order:										
Can name in random order:										
Can match number of objects to numeral:										

Writing numerals	yes	no	date
Can draw a circle freehand			
Can copy a square			
Can copy a triangle			

	1	2	3	4	5	6	7	8	9
Can copy these numerals:									
Can draw these numerals freehand:									

NOTE

If any of the numerals are incorrectly copied or reversed, enter the child's version in the appropriate space with date, e.g. ſ or Ɛ

The four rules from one to ten									yes	no	date
Understands the meaning of 'more' in practical setting											
Understands the meaning of 'less' in practical setting											
	1	2	3	4	5	6	7	8	9			
Can add one more to:												
One less than:												
Knows the number bonds of:												
Can use bonds for addition												
Can use bonds for subtraction												
	2s	3s	4s	5s	10s							
Can count in:												
Can solve practical problems with counting in twos, etc.:												

	2	3	4	5	6	7	8	9	10	11	12
Can add scores by counting on to a total of:											
Can add the numbers on two dice to a total of:											

The number ten	yes	no
Knows the number bonds of ten		
Recognises and names 10p and a 1p coin		
Knows that ten 1p coins have the same value as one 10p coin		

From a 10p coin knows how much change after spending	1p.	2p.	3p.	4p.	5p.	6p.	7p.	8p.	9p.

	yes	no
Recognises numerals up to ten		
Recognises the plus sign (+) and the equals sign (=)		
Can work out addition sums written down up to a total of ten either, with cards or sticks:		
Without cards or sticks:		

SECTION THREE CHECKLIST

Introduction to tables
Can count in: 2s   3s   4s   5s   10s
Knows tables: 2x   3x   4x   5x   10x
Uses tables: 2x   3x   4x   5x   10x
(ring the appropriate number)

More than ten
Can count from one to: 10 11 12 13 14 15 16 17 18 19 20
(ring number reached)

Can bundle sticks in tens with spare sticks and know the total	10 11 12 13 14 15 16 17 18 19
Can work out pictorial sums as above	10 11 12 13 14 15 16 17 18 19
Can work out written sums to:	10 11 12 13 14 15 16 17 18 19

Counting in tens
Counts in tens to: 10 20 30 40 50 60 70 80 90 100
Can read these from
figures: 10 20 30 40 50 60 70 80 90 100
Can write these: 10 20 30 40 50 60 70 80 90 100
Can bundle sticks
with spare sticks
and know the total 10+ 20+ 30+ 40+ 50+ 60+ 70+ 80+ 90+100
Can write the total
in tens and units
e.g. 24, 67, 49, etc.   10+ 20+ 30+ 40+ 50+ 60+ 70+ 80+ 90+
(ring the figure reached in each case)

Addition of tens and units without carrying	yes	no	date
Can arrange two rows of 10p and 1p coins in order, i.e. 10ps on the left and 1ps on the right and add them up			
Can do the arrangement above and record as conventional addition sums without carrying.			
Can work out conventional addition sums with the aid of apparatus (money, bundles and sticks, etc.)			
Can work out conventional addition sums without using apparatus (no carrying)			
Use of calculators Can press the right keys on a calculator to get single numbers			
Can press the keys in the right order for a number with tens and units, e.g. 56 or 89			
Knows and meaning of the + sign on the calculator			
Knows the meaning of the = sign on the calculator			
Can add together two single numbers on the calculator, e.g. $7+4$ and get the answer, 11			
Can add together two numbers involving tens and units on the calculator (no carrying)			
Can use the calculator to check own addition sums with tens and units			
Knows the meaning of the — sign, i.e. take away, less			

	yes	no	date
Can check simple subtraction sums involving single numbers on the calculator			
Can check simple subtraction sums on the calculator, tens and units			
Can use the calculator to check the change from shopping			
Can use the calculator to check cost of purchases			

More multiplication

Can count in:	2s	3s	4s	5s	6s	7s	8s	9s	10s
Knows tables:	2x	3x	4x	5x	6x	7x	8x	9x	10x
Uses tables:	2x	3x	4x	5x	6x	7x	8x	9x	10x

(ring the appropriate number)

Fractions	yes	no	date
Can halve an apple or cake			
Can fold a sheet of paper in half			
Can cut a slab of margarine in half			
Knows that when you halve you get two pieces			
Understands practically the meaning of a quarter by folding or cutting a whole object			
Recognises segments of circles (ring the appropriate ones) $\frac{1}{2}$ $\frac{1}{4}$ $\frac{1}{6}$ $\frac{1}{12}$			
Can recognise half past the hour on a clockface			
Can recognise a quarter past the hour on a clockface			

	yes	no	date
Can recognise a quarter to on a clockface			
Can find the value of half of a number of things practically, e.g. half of sixteen			
Can find the value of a quarter of a number of things practically, e.g. a quarter of twenty			
Can find the value of a third of a number of things practically, e.g. a third of twenty-one			
Can find the value of a sixth of a number of things practically . . . a sixth of thirty			
Can find the value of a fifth of a number of things practically, e.g. a fifth of twenty			
Can find the value of a tenth of a number of things practically			
Other fractions which are used practically —note which			
Can use knowledge of fractions in other lessons, e.g. cookery, to find amounts of ingredients, etc.			

SECTION FOUR CHECKLIST

Time	yes	no	date
Has regular pattern of sleeping and waking			
Anticipates daily events, e.g. meal times			
Shows by behaviour that he knows the difference between weekdays and weekends			
Can use an egg timer or ping timer to time own tasks			
Can list the daily meals in order			
Recognises where the hour hand will be on a clockface at breakfast time, lunch time, teatime, supper, etc. (at least four different times in the day)			
Can read the hours on a clock and move the hands appropriately			
Knows where the minute hand will be at half-past the hour			
Can tell the time at half-past any hour			
Knows where the minute hand will be at a quarter past the hour			
Can tell the time at a quarter past any hour			
Knows where the minute hand will be at a quarter to the hour			
Can tell the time at a quarter to the hour			
Can tell the time to the nearest five minutes			
Can time self on the clock in quarter hours			
Can time self on the clock in five-minute intervals			

	yes	no	date
Can tell the time on clocks with different faces			
Can tell the time on a digital clock			
Days of the week Knows that having a sleep must come before 'tomorrow'			
Can talk about what took place 'yesterday' and 'today'			
Looks forward to events in the near future, e.g. swimming, visiting relations, etc., and can wait for them without pestering			
Looks forward to events which are some weeks or months away, e.g. birthdays, half-term, Christmas, etc., and has at least some idea of how long to wait			
Knows the names of the days of the week but not in order			
Knows the names of the days of the week in order			
Knows which day of the week starts the weekend			
Knows which day a favourite programme is broadcast or a favourite lesson at school			
Can tell which day of the week it is on any one day			
Knows that a week has seven days			
Knows that a fortnight is two weeks			
Knows that a fortnight has fourteen days			

	yes	no	date
The year Can tell the four months of the year in order			
Knows what to expect in spring, summer, autumn and winter to some extent, e.g. lambs, sea bathing, leaf fall, snow!			
Knows the names of some of the yearly festivals, e.g. Easter, Christmas, Hallowe'en			
Knows the names of the months but not necessarily in the right order			
Knows the names of the months in the right order			
Knows the month of own birthday			
Can read the date			
Can write the date			
Knows the number of days in each month			
Ages Knows own age in years			
Can put family photos of self when a baby, infant, school girl/boy in chronological order			
Can work out the difference in ages in years			
Can 'read' correctly 1986, 1987, 1988, etc.			
Knows how to write the current year			
Knows own date of birth in day, month and year			
Knows today's date in day, month and year			

	yes	no	date
Length Can compare two lengths, e.g. of string, and say which is longer and which is shorter			
Can compare more than two lengths and say which is the longest and which is the shortest			
Can tell you how much longer one row of bricks is than another in number of bricks			
Can measure other things using bricks, paperclips, handspans, etc., as units of measurement, and tell the length in bricks, paperclips, etc.			
Can compare heights from marks on the wall and understands 'higher' and 'highest' and 'shorter' and 'shortest'			
Can use a standard measure to measure lengths using a simple ruler in two colours, and gives the length correctly in inches or centimetres			
Can use a measure to measure length, width, depth and height			
Can measure round objects, e.g. heads or waists			
Can use measuring tapes, etc., for practical purposes, e.g. to find sizes for garments or a garden plot			
Has some idea of relative distances travelled			

	yes	no	date
Weight, capacity and volume Can fill containers right up to the top with sand, for instance, and knows what is meant by 'full' and 'empty'			
Can accurately measure out quantities of sand, sawdust, rice, flour, etc., into a container, using an improvised measure (carton, spoon, cup) and keep a tally of the number of cups/spoonfuls that have gone in			
Can dilute concentrated fruit juice accurately by using an improvised measure			
Can use a standard pint-sized bottle for practical measures in the cookery session			
Can use a standard measuring jug in the cookery lesson and choose the appropriate measure for rice, flour, liquid, etc.			
Understands that when two things balance they weigh the same			
Understands how to fill the pans of a balancing scale until the two pans are horizontal			
Can use a standard weight (one ounce) to measure goods (sweets, etc.) accurately on balancing scales			
Knows how many ounces make a pound and can measure out a pound of goods in one ounce weights			
Can use two different standard weights and measure goods in pounds and ounces			
Can use bathrooms scales and read the weight of a friend			

	yes	no	date
Can calculate amounts of ingredients in a recipe for half the printed number			
Can calculate the ingredients for a quarter of the printed number			
Can read off metric weights on the scales			
Shapes Can fit two shapes into a posting box or form-board without help, i.e. sphere and cube (circle and square)			
Can fit four or more shapes into a posting box or form-board without help			
Can sort objects of different sizes according to shape (pyramids, cubes, spheres, cuboids, etc.)			
Can pick out a cube, sphere or cylinder from other shapes when asked			
Can name a cube, sphere (ball), cylinder, and cuboid (brick shape) when asked			
Recognises examples of the above shapes in the street			
Can match squares, circles, triangles, rectangles, either from cards or in a form-board			
Can pick out squares, circles, triangles, rectangles			
Can name squares, circles, triangles, rectangles			
Recognises that the same number of cubes can be used to make different shapes			
Knows that the number of cubes in a given shape is called its volume			

	yes	no	date
Is familiar with the idea of cubic centimetres or inches. Can measure the volume of a cuboid or cube which is in whole numbers			
Understands the meaning of capacity			
Can work out the area of rectangles drawn on squared paper			
Can work out the area of box lids, etc., using a simple ruler (either inches or centimetres) and whole numbers			
Can work out the area of a plot of land or room in strides (i.e. square strides)			
Can work out the area of a plot of land or room using a simple measuring tape			
Can make a plan of a plot of land or room on squared paper			
Money values and shopping Understands how tokens earned for good behaviour or how work can be exchanged for goodies			
Understands how pennies earned for good behaviour or work can be exchanged for goodies at the school or corner shop			
Coins Can sort out and match ten pence and one penny coins			
Can point to ten pence or one penny coins from a display of coins			
Can name ten pence and one penny coins			

	yes	no	date
Knows that ten 1p coins have the same value as one 10p coin			
Can sort out and match ten pence, two pence and one penny coins			
Can name ten pence, two pence and one penny coins			
Knows how many two pence coins make ten pence			
Can sort out and match ten pence, five pence, two pence and one penny coins			
Can identify and name ten pence, five pence, two pence and one penny coins			
Can change appropriate assortments of coppers and five pence coins for a ten pence coin			
Can sort out and match fifty pence, ten pence, five pence, two pence and one penny coins			
Can identify and name fifty pence, ten pence, five pence, two pence and one penny coins			
Can identify and name a one pound coin and knows that this is equal in value to two fifty pence coins			
Shopping Knows how to look for and find an article on the supermarket shelves			
Can find appropriate coins in purse to pay for an item up to ten pence in price			
Can find appropriate coins in purse to pay for any item less then fifty pence in price			

	yes	no	date
Can find appropriate coins in purse to pay for any item less than one pound in price			
Can check change from a ten pence piece			
Can check change from a fifty pence piece			
Combines coins and notes to give a specified amount of money			
Keeps a written record of amount spent on several items			
Can tot up the amount spent on several items with an abacus or other structured apparatus			
Can tot up the amount of money spent without using abacus, etc.			
Can use a calculator to check the amount of money spent			
Has regular pocket money/wages and can budget for daily expenses			
Uses a piggy bank to save up for special treats			
Understands and uses a simple saving scheme			

FURTHER READING AND REFERENCES

BRUNER, J. S., JOLLY, A. and SYLVA, K. (1976) *Play.*
Harmondsworth: Penguin.

CANWELL, P. (1987) *Counting Songs.* Early Learning Centre.

DOMAN, G. (1979) *Teach Your Baby Maths.* London: Jonathan
Cape.

GILLHAM, B. (1987) *A Basic Attainments Programme for Young
Mentally Handicapped Children.* London: Croom Helm.

GRAHAM, A. T. (1985) *Help Your Child with Maths.* London:
Fontana.

GRIFFITHS, R. (1988) *Maths through Play.* London: Macdonald.

HARGREAVES, J. (1986) *Cookery for Handicapped People.*
London: Souvenir Press.

HARWOOD, A. C. (1958) *The Recovery of Man in Childhood.*
London: Hodder & Stoughton.

JEFFREE, D. and CHESELDINE, S. (1985) *Pathways to Independence.* Sevenoaks: Hodder & Stoughton.

JEFFREE, D. and CHESELDINE, S. (1984) *Let's Join In.* London:
Souvenir Press.

LADYBIRD SERIES. *Learning with Traditional Rhymes.* Loughborough: Ladybird Books.

LIEBECK, P. (1984) *How Children Learn Mathematics.* London:
Penguin.

MATTHEWS, G. & J. (1978) 'Apparatus, Toys and Games'.
Booklet from *Early Mathematical Experiences.* Schools
Council Project. Addison & Wesley.

McCONKEY, R. and McEVOY. J. (1986) *Count Me In.* Video
course obtainable from The Librarian, Ulster Polytechnic,
Newtownabbey, Co. Antrim, N. Ireland.

McCONKEY, R. and McEVOY, J. (1986) 'Games for learning to
count'. *British Journal of Special Education, 13,* 2, 59-62.

MERTTENS, R. (1987) *The Parent and Child Programme.* 59,
Grosvenor Street, London. (A series of booklets for parents
on teaching mathematics.)

NEWSON, J. and E. (1979) *Toys and Playthings*. London: George Allen & Unwin.

RODGERS, S. C. (1988) *Teaching Practical Nameracy to Handicapped Children*. London: Routledge.

TIZARD, B. and HUGHES, M. (1984) *Young Children Learning*. London: Fontana.

WOMAK, D. (1988) *Developing Mathematical and Scientific Thinking in Young Children*. London: Cassell.

SUPPLIERS

Arnold/ESA, Parkside Lane, Dewsbury, Leeds LSU 5TD.

Brio Scanditoy Ltd., Belton Road West, Loughborough, Leicestershire.

Early Learning Centre, South Marston, Swindon SN3 4TJ.

Escor Toys Ltd., Groveley Road, Christchurch BH23 3RQ.

Galt, James & Co. Ltd., Brookfield Road, Cheadle, Cheshire.

Invicta Plastics Ltd., Oadby, Leicestershire.

LDA, Duke Street, Wisbech, Cambridgeshire.

Living and Learning, 32, Bridge Street, Cambridge CB2 1UJ.

Philip & Tacey Ltd., North Way, Andover, Hampshire SP10 5BA.

Ravensburger (Fisher Price Toys Ltd.) Lilliput Road, Brackmill Industrial Estate, Northampton.

Spear, J. W. & Sons Ltd., P.O. Box 49, Enfield, Middlesex EN3 7SF.

Toys For The Handicapped, 76 Barracks Road, Sandy Lane Industrial Estate, Stourport-on-Severn, Worcestershire DY13 9QB.

Waddingtons Playing Card Company, Wakefield Road, Leeds LS10 3TP.

Willis Toys Ltd., Robin Hood Road, Elsenham. Bishops Stortford CM22 6EF.

INDEX